History of the Mathematics of
Certainty and Chance

Pathways to Probability

Amy C. King

Cecil B. Read

Holt, Rinehart and Winston, Inc., New York

HOLT, RINEHART AND WINSTON, INC.

All Rights Reserved

Printed in the United States of America

17764-1013
Copyright 1963

Preface

In many books dealing with the elementary aspects of probability there is little or no attention paid to the discussion of how our present theories have been developed. Who is it that is responsible for the methods, rules, theorems and other concepts which we now have at our disposal? What kind of men were the explorers in this new field? Did they make any mistakes? Did they, like Columbus, think they had found a new route to a solution when in reality they were on the verge of the discovery of unknown territory? It may be of interest to see something of the non-mathematical side of the lives of a few of these individuals. Was the study of probability their major interest in mathematics or a minor part of their career? Quite possibly there is no better way to make mathematics seem alive than through a study of the biographies of its founders.

Anyone going to a large university library to look for available books on the subject of probability will find that here is a topic which may require some advanced mathematical background. In fact, at the present time this is one of the most rapidly growing fields in mathematics. There is no intent in this book to cover to any extent those phases of probability which might be termed "advanced." Rather the emphasis will be on what might be called "elementary concepts of probability." Since even this term may mean different things to different people, a further clarification would be that the subject material is essentially restricted to those concepts which could be presented in a secondary school course for students with no further background than advanced algebra. However, with a few minor exceptions, the material is suitable to those with practically no mathematical background, and at the same time may be of interest to those with more extensive training.

The presentation will be primarily chronological. There will be an attempt to understand the development of probability through an understanding of the men who were working in the subject, together with conditions existing at the time, limitations imposed by these conditions, as well as the state of development of mathematical theory. In other words this is indeed a study of the various *Pathways to Probability* and in turn how these have led into the related fields of statistics.

The authors would like to acknowledge the following people who have read and helped in the preparation of this book: Maurine L. Gist, Don R. King, and Beverly Jean Read.

Contents

1

Are The Odds Against You?

For almost as long as man has lived on earth there has been interest in the question, "Are the Odds Against You?" Certainly there has been a written record of the study of this and similar questions for at least five hundred years.

The Areas of Probability

Inquiries like the following, which involve many aspects of life, often arise: If a player has a batting average of 0.300 in baseball, what are the chances that he will get two hits in his next three times at bat? Is a total of seven points more likely than a total of five points when two dice are thrown? If seven is more likely, what are the odds in its favor? Is it true that if one tosses a coin enough times, heads and tails are sure to come up the same number of times? Are there any uses of probability other than in the study of games of chance? What are the odds against a man aged twenty living to be seventy? If a new vaccine seems to prevent a disease in ninety out of one hundred cases in which the vaccine is administered, what are the chances that if one is treated with the vaccine he will not contract the disease? What are the chances that the next baby born in a family will be a girl? What are the chances if the preceding four children have all been girls? What are the chances of finding a four-leaf clover? Is it true that lightning never strikes twice in the same place? If it is known that a particular intersection has had five "fender-benders" in the past month, what is the probability of your having an accident if you drive through this intersection? What is the probability that an intercontinental ballistic missile will land within one mile of its intended target? What is the probability that a missile aimed at a certain spot on the moon will land within ten miles of its intended point of impact? (See Fig. 1-1.)

As one may see from the preceding queries, the subject of probability appears in many fields, such as business, insurance, biology, genetics, medicine, manufacturing, as well as in games of chance.

Fig. 1-1

What is Probability?

Before discussing a subject it is necessary to be familiar with the terms we are using. At the present time there are several definitions of probability, two of which we shall consider. The classical, *mathematical*, or a priori, states that if an event can happen in n different ways, all of which are equally likely, and if f of these results are defined as favorable, the probability of a favorable result is f/n. To illustrate this definition, suppose we have in a box:

$$1 \text{ red ball}$$
$$2 \text{ white balls}$$
$$6 \text{ green balls}$$
$$\overline{\phantom{9 \text{ balls total}}}$$
$$9 \text{ balls total}$$

If we define the drawing of a green ball as a favorable event, the probability of drawing a green ball would be 6/9. In like manner the probability of drawing a white ball would be 2/9, and of a red ball 1/9. This definition represents the point of view generally held by the early workers in the theory of probability.

A second viewpoint is called *statistical, experimental,* or *theoretical,* and is based on relative frequency, or what is known to have happened in the past. If an automobile insurance company finds that in a certain city eight cars are stolen each year out of every one thousand that are insured, the probability of a car being stolen is defined to be 8/1000. Suppose past experience has shown that of 100,000 people alive at the age of ten years, only three lived to celebrate their ninety-fifth birthday. The probability of a person aged ten reaching this age would then be 3/100,000 or 0.00003.

Rules. Before a person plays a game he must know the rules, and before undertaking the study of any subject it is necessary to have information about some of the basic concepts. However, just as it is possible for a person to watch a game without knowing all the rules, it is also possible for a person not having much mathematical training to read this book without going into all the details.

What do we really mean when we ask, "Are the Odds Against You?" If an event may happen in five different ways, for example, three being successful and two unsuccessful, then it is said the odds are three to two in favor of the event being a success. If only one way is considered a success, then we say the odds are one to four against success.

What do we mean by *mutually exclusive*? In our previous example if one draws one ball and it is white, this precludes the possibility of its being a red ball, or if one tosses a coin and it falls "heads," this excludes the possibility of "tails." In other words, if one occurs the other cannot. In drawing cards from a deck, the drawing of a spade and of a heart are mutually exclusive, since if in a single draw a heart occurs, this excludes the possibility of drawing a spade. To illustrate the rules used in dealing with mutually exclusive events, let us refer to the box where we had one red ball, two white ones, and six green. If one were asked the probability p of drawing either a red ball *or* a white ball in one draw, this is the sum of the probabilities, that is:

$$p = \frac{1 + 2}{9} = 1/9 + 2/9 = 3/9.$$

It will be seen that success can be either a red ball (one possibility) or a white ball (two possibilities). Hence there are three events which are considered a success out of nine possible events or ways to draw the ball. The probability of either a red or white ball is the sum of the probability of drawing a red ball and the probability of drawing a white ball.

If one were asked the probability p of drawing a red ball first *and* then a white ball, replacing the ball after each draw, we might consider that in the long run, one-ninth of the time a red ball will be drawn. If a red ball is not drawn on the first draw, we need not proceed further. If a red ball is drawn, with probability one-ninth, then in the long run in two-ninths of these cases a white ball will be drawn. The probability is hence

$$p = (1/9) \, (2/9) = 2/81.$$

We thus see that the result is equivalent to multiplication of the respective probabilities. An extension may be made to any number, if we are dealing with mutually exclusive events. The key words *either* and *or* give the *sum* of the independent probabilities. In the second case the key words are *and* and *both* and they give the *product* of the individual probabilities.

What do we mean by *independent* events? If the occurrence of one event does not affect the occurrence of the other, then we have independent events. If the names of members of a class are placed on cards in a box, and one name is drawn, the card being replaced, the result of this drawing does not affect the result of a second drawing. On the other hand if we draw one card from a deck of fifty-two playing cards, and then draw a second card without replacing the first card, the probability of the second card being a heart is *dependent* upon the first card drawn.

When Are the Odds Against You?

That all depends on the game you are playing. One can rest assured that if a game is played with a person who makes his living on "games of chance" that truly the odds are very much against you. In fact most people would be astounded at these odds, even in so-called honest games. In throwing a die, one's chance of obtaining a two is 1/6. In this case the odds are against you five to one. The chance of a person now twenty living to be seventy is 38,569/92,637 or approximately .416. The odds against you are 54,068 to 38,569. Here we already see better odds than in the game with the die. These figures and similar ones may be obtained from Mortality Tables which are based on previous experience. In business a manufacturer makes huge samplings to see in what way the trend of public opinion is moving. By the theory of probability one can sometimes predict the price and style of a commodity which will sell. Needless to say there are many factors which are involved in some of these investigations, but it is astonishing to find the many facets of our lives in which we find probability and its related field, statistics.

In the following chapter we will find some of the very earliest workers in the field of probability, and in succeeding chapters we will see how the theory of probability evolved, through
the lives, accomplishments, and difficulties of some of the men
who made it possible.

2

Early Glimpses

Cardan: Two Sides on One Coin

There now seems to be a growing feeling that *Jerome Cardan* (Gerolamo Cardano, 1501–1576, Italian, Fig. 2-1) was the real pioneer in the field of probability. This branch of mathematics could not have begun with a more colorful personality. The fact that at times his reputation was not above reproach may explain why many years passed before he was credited with making the real beginning, and also why it was so long before probability was considered a true science.

Cardan was the son of a lawyer and professor of medicine in Milan. He was educated at the universities of Pavia and Padua. It was during 1524–1550, while a practicing physician,

Scripta Mathematica

Fig. 2-1.   Jerome Cardan.

that he published his chief works. He wrote on mathematics, games of chance, astronomy, physics, death, and other things.

Cardan is reported to have been quick-tempered and sometimes unable to control his anger. His genius bordered on insanity; and at times he was involved in brawls of the most serious kind, once being put in prison for publishing the horoscope of Christ.

His book, *Liber de Ludo Aleae* or "Book on Games of Chance," which is really a gambler's manual, is considered by many to be the first book on probability. Among other things he discusses in it are how many successes in how many trials, additive properties of probabilities, and what we would now term mathematical expectation. Additive properties were noted in Chapter 1, the key words being *either* and *or*. By mathematical expectation we mean the product of the probability that an event will happen multiplied by the value of the event. For example, if a person would win $1.00 if he tossed a coin and it came up heads his mathematical expectation would be ($1.00) (1/2) or fifty cents. Not only does Cardan give applications of his theories, but he further philosophizes, giving advice to those with lesser experience than the veteran author. The book contains descriptions of gambling games, his favorite pastime and main source of income in his youth, and also includes tips on how to cheat and avoid being cheated.

He correctly shows the number of ways that two dice may be thrown, noting that with two dice there is only one way in which a two or a twelve may be thrown, two ways of throwing a three or an eleven, three ways of throwing a four or a ten, four ways of throwing a five or a nine, five ways of throwing a six or an eight, and six ways of throwing a seven. These possible outcomes are shown in the accompanying table.

Cardan further lists the ways in which three dice may fall. Thus, there is only one way of throwing a three, with a one on each face; three ways each of throwing a total of four or seventeen; and so on.

As a dramatic ending to this many-sided personality Cardan predicted the day of his death. When the day arrived he was still alive, so he committed suicide to preserve his reputation.

Total of Numbers Appearing	Specific Numbers Showing on Each Face	
	Die No. 1	Die No. 2
Two	1	1
Three	1 2	2 1
Four	1 2 3	3 2 1
Five	1 2 3 4	4 3 2 1
Six	1 2 3 4 5	5 4 3 2 1
Seven	1 2 3 4 5 6	6 5 4 3 2 1
Eight	2 3 4 5 6	6 5 4 3 2
Nine	3 4 5 6	6 5 4 3
Ten	4 5 6	6 5 4
Eleven	5 6	6 5
Twelve	6	6

The Great Galileo

Galileo Galilei (1564–1642, Italian) was born the son of a Florentine nobleman. The medical profession, which was very highly paid, appealed to Galileo's family. At seventeen he went to the University of Pisa to study for his medical degree. Prior to this he had been ignorant of mathematics and the other sciences. His interest in science began when he heard a lecture on geometry which so intrigued him that he decided to spend his leisure in its study. With parental permission he discontinued his medical studies and began original research. He had noticed a lamp, still hanging in the cathedral of Pisa, which was being moved in order to light it. When it was released the swinging back and forth was at first considerable but gradually decreased. The oscillations seemed, however, to be made in equal periods of time, an observation he confirmed as he timed them by counting his pulse. Thus, he was able to establish this important property of the pendulum.

Galileo is sometimes called the greatest Italian physicist, astronomer, and mathematician of his time, and one of the greatest in the world. He was a very popular lecturer and his demonstrations were said to be so charming that he drew capacity crowds of over two thousand people.

Although he was early drawn to the Copernican system in which the planets were believed to revolve around the sun, it was not until about 1605, at the appearance of a new star, that he openly renounced the idea of an earth-centered universe. He was told by a high ecclesiastical authority to write freely, provided what he wrote had nothing to do with religion. In 1616 the Inquisition declared that to suppose the sun to be the center of the solar system was false and opposed Holy Scripture. Publication of a book by Galileo was approved by a papal censor, but the content was contrary to the Edict of 1616, and Galileo was summoned to Rome. He was forced to publicly renounce his theories, do penance, and was released only on promise of obedience. It is said that at the time of the public denial he whispered "but it does go round it anyway."

He retired to a small village near Florence where he wrote and meditated until his death at the age of seventy-eight.

Of the problems in probability on which Galileo worked, the following is perhaps the most famous. With three dice the numbers nine and ten can each be produced by six different combinations.

Combinations for Producing the Numbers
Nine and Ten with Three Dice

Ways to obtain Nine	Ways to obtain Ten
1, 2, 6	1, 3, 6
1, 3, 5	1, 4, 5
1, 4, 4	2, 2, 6
2, 2, 5	2, 3, 5
2, 3, 4	2, 4, 4
3, 3, 3	3, 3, 4

It is seen that order is important, and this will be discussed in the next chapter under *permutations* and *combinations*.

Total Combinations for Ten			Total Combinations for Nine		
Die No. 1	Die No. 2	Die No. 3	Die No. 1	Die No. 2	Die No. 3
1	3	6	1	2	6
1	4	5	1	6	2
1	6	3	1	3	5
1	5	4	1	5	3
2	2	6	1	4	4
2	6	2	2	1	6
2	3	5	2	6	1
2	5	3	2	2	5
2	4	4	2	5	2
3	6	1	2	3	4
3	1	6	2	4	3
3	5	2	3	1	5
3	2	5	3	5	1
3	4	3	3	2	4
3	3	4	3	4	2
4	1	5	3	3	3
4	5	1	4	1	4
4	2	4	4	4	1
4	4	2	4	2	3
4	3	3	4	3	2
5	1	4	5	1	3
5	4	1	5	3	1
5	2	3	5	2	2
5	3	2	6	1	2
6	1	3	6	2	1
6	3	1			
6	2	2			

From experience the number ten appeared more often. Galileo analyzed all cases carefully and showed that out of the 6^3 or 216 total ways the three dice could be thrown there are twenty-seven ways favorable for ten, but only twenty-five favorable to the appearance of nine (See table, p. 17). Thus, the results from the theory of probability coincided with experimental values obtained. These are only two of the many early workers in probability, and although approximately fifty years had now elapsed from the time of Cardan's studies until the work of Galileo, the latter treatment did not show the range or depth of that done by Cardan.

The statement is frequently encountered that the study of probability began with correspondence between Pascal and Fermat, which we shall discuss in the next chapter. However, without in any way belittling the contributions of these men, it should be pointed out that for roughly a century before their time, mathematicians of no little repute had devoted considerable time to a study of certain more or less elementary aspects of the subject of probability.

3

Arrangements and Combinations

In a *permutation* order is important, and in a *combination* order is immaterial. In general from a set of n objects, we may form more permutations of three objects than combinations of three objects. This is also true for a selection of four objects, and so on. Formulas for the number of permutations or combinations are available in standard texts. Using such formulas one finds that if, for example, five colors are chosen from the colors red, white, blue, green, yellow, and black, there are six different combinations, but there are 720 different permutations possible.

As we shall see later, the theories of permutations, combinations, and probability have very practical uses. The actual study of the theory of probability, as well as that of permutations and combinations, is often said to have begun in a correspondence between Pascal and Fermat.

Pascal: Only Thirty-Nine Years

Blaise Pascal (1623–1662, French, Fig. 3-2) has been described by several authors as the greatest "might-have-been" in the history of mathematics. When he was one year old he was stricken with a serious illness, and at one time his family thought he was dead. The illness was blamed on a sorceress, who was persuaded to lift her spell. Pascal remained frail throughout his entire life and never attended school with other children; perhaps for this reason it seemed hard for him to get along with other people, and he maintained an apartness from the world. In 1631 the family moved to Paris to enable his father to pursue his own scientific studies, and to give Pascal greater opportunity to further his education.

19

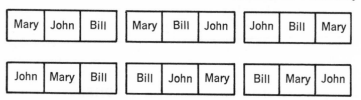

Fig. 3-1. Since each of the above arrangements consists of the same children, we have only one "combination," but there are six different "permutations."

Pascal's curiosity about mathematics was aroused at this time. When he was twelve years old he asked his tutor what geometry was and received the reply that it is the science of constructing exact figures and then determining the proportions between their different parts. According to his sister he then duplicated thirty-two of Euclid's propositions. The probability of an exact duplication is of course very doubtful. At the age of fourteen his father took him to weekly scientific discussions. When he was sixteen he had published a tiny treatise on conic sections which was such an accomplishment that the mathematician Descartes refused to believe that it had been written by Pascal.

Fig. 3.2. Blaise Pascal.

Scripta Mathematica

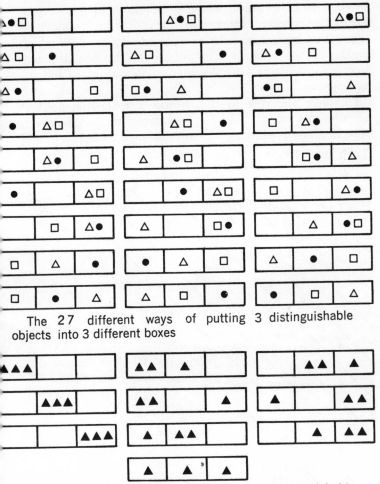

The 27 different ways of putting 3 distinguishable objects into 3 different boxes

The 10 different ways of putting 3 indistinguishable objects into 3 different boxes

The 1 way of putting 3 indisinguishable objects into 3 different boxes when no box can contain more than 1 object

Fig. 3-3. Three different types of permutations.

When his father enlisted Pascal's help in totaling tax assessments, Pascal was so distraught with adding long columns of figures that he lent his talents to inventing a machine which could add and subtract. The result was the first definitely recorded calculating machine, if we ignore the abacus and our ten fingers.

For three centuries before his birth "Pascal's triangle" had actually been known and used. It is named for him, however, since he discovered many hitherto unknown relationships and properties about it. It is an array of numbers which may be written in the following form:

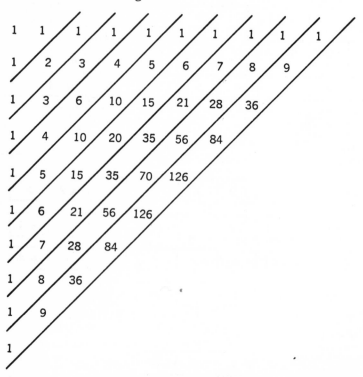

Note that no diagonal is drawn after the very first entry. If we want to find the number of combinations of n things taken r at a time we look above the nth diagonal and the $(r + 1)$

column. Thus for the number of combinations of nine items taken four at a time we may look above the ninth diagonal and up this diagonal from the left to the $(r + 1)$ item. This is found to be 126. The result may also be obtained from the formula $C(9,4) = 126$.

A second way of illustrating this triangle is as follows:

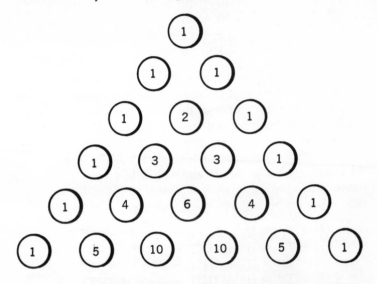

In this arrangement it may be noted that the numbers in the nth row, disregarding the top one, are the coefficients of the expansion $(x + y)^n$ by the binomial theorem. Thus $(x + y)^2 = x^2 + 2xy + y^2$, the coefficients being 1, 2, 1. In the expansion $(x + y)^3 = x^3 + 3x^2y + 3xy^2 + y^3$, the coefficients are 1, 3, 3, 1, etc. The numbers in the nth row, again disregarding the top one, are the number of different selections of one, two, three, . . . items selected from n distinct items. For example, suppose the third row is chosen. The number of combinations of three things taken zero at a time is one; the number taken one at a time is three; the number taken two at a time is three; and the number taken three at a time is one. In this row we find the numbers 1, 3, 3, 1 as stated. Another property in the second arrangement is that any number is the sum of the numbers to the left and to the right of the above numbers. Therefore, the next row of the triangle would be computed as follows:

$$
\begin{aligned}
0 + 1 &= 1 \\
1 + 5 &= 6 \\
5 + 10 &= 15 \\
10 + 10 &= 20 \\
10 + 5 &= 15 \\
5 + 1 &= 6 \\
1 + 0 &= 1.
\end{aligned}
$$

It might be interesting to note some additional relations such as the sum of the numbers along the nth diagonal is 2^n. The number in the nth row and the rth column is equal to the number in the rth row and the nth column. The reader may want to find additional properties.

As a further application of "Pascal's triangle" we might consider the number of heads and tails when several coins are tossed simultaneously. Let H represent heads and T represent tails. From the binomial theorem we have:

$$
\begin{aligned}
(H + T) &= H + T \\
(H + T)^2 &= H^2 + 2H\,T + T^2 \\
(H + T)^3 &= H^3 + 3H^2T + 3H\,T^2 + T^3 \\
(H + T)^4 &= H^4 + 4H^3T + 6H^2T^2 + 4HT^3 + T^4 \\
\cdots\cdots\cdots &= \cdots\cdots\cdots\cdots\cdots\cdots\cdots\cdots\cdots\cdots\cdots\cdots\cdots\cdots\cdots\cdots
\end{aligned}
$$

It can be shown that the coefficients of the various terms of these expansions (which are the numbers in the proper row of the Pascal triangle) give the relative frequency of occurrence of the various possibilities. To illustrate, if four coins are tossed, we would expect to find on the average two heads and two tails (H^2T^2) six times as frequently as four heads (H^4). Also since the coefficients of the terms H^2T^2 and HT^3, representing "two heads, two tails" and "one head, three tails" respectively, are six and four, we would expect one and one-half times as many occurrences of "two heads, two tails" as of "one head, three tails." Since the probability of a head is one-half, and the probability of a tail is one-half, then in the case of three coins the probability of two heads and one tail is given by $3H^2T = 3(1/2)^2(1/2) = 3/8$.

Pascal's triangle was only one relatively minor aspect of his development of the theory of probability. As has been mentioned, much of this new theory arose from correspondence between Pascal and Fermat. However, Pascal was one of the first to violate the laws of this new theory of probability, which holds that accidents and coincidences are the workings of natural laws.

During the latter part of the year 1654 he was riding in a carriage when the horses suddenly started running away. He was narrowly saved from death, so he thought, by the traces breaking. This he interpreted as a sign that his scientific studies were displeasing to God, so he entered a Jansenist community. In 1658 he had a terrible toothache and the ache disappeared while he was meditating about the cycloid, which is a curve represented by the path of a point on the rim of a rolling wheel. This relief from pain Pascal interpreted as a sign to return to his scientific work. He worked incessantly for eight days on the cycloid. This was his last contribution to science but was rich in mathematical and physical ideas and played an important role in the early development of the calculus.

It is said that from the age of seventeen until his death he passed but few days without pain. He never married, and died at the age of thirty-nine. If ever a truly gifted man buried his talents, Pascal did, but in spite of this he left a name in literature, mathematics, and physics which is still respected after more than three centuries.

Fermat: His Favorite Hobby

Pierre de Fermat (c. 1608–1665, French, Fig. 3-4) shares equally with Pascal in the credit for putting the theory of probability on a scientific basis. His father was a leather merchant and his mother the daughter of a family of lawyers. His earliest education was received at home and later he went to Toulouse to prepare for a career in law. His entire thirty-four

Scripta Mathematica

Fig. 3-4. Pierre de Fermat.

years of working life was devoted to the exacting service of the state and to his favorite hobby, mathematics. He was the founder of modern number theory. The true beauty of his discoveries lies in the fact that any good high school student can readily understand, but perhaps not prove, many of them. A few examples are listed:

1. Every odd prime can be presented in one and only one way as the difference of two squares.

2. A prime of the form $4n + 1$ can be represented as the sum of two squares.

3. Every non-negative integer can be expressed as the sum of four or fewer squares.

4. There is only one solution in integers of $x^2 + 2 = y^3$ and only two of $x^2 + 4 = y^3$. This problem was given as a challenge problem to English mathematicians. The solutions are $x = 5$ and $y = 3$ for the first and $x = 2$ and $y = 2$ or $x = 11$, $y = 5$ for the second.

Most of Fermat's work is to be found in the margins of the book he was reading at the time or in the voluminous correspondence which he carried on. Without these sources much, if not all, of what he did would have been lost. He did not seem inclined to use systematic procedures or to publish his results but merely jotted things down for his own benefit. Rarely did he give any hint as to his method of proof. It is reported that one outstanding mathematician worked off and on for some seven years in discovering the proof of one of Fermat's propositions. His "Last Theorem" has baffled amateur and professional alike to this day. It states that for an integer n greater than two, one cannot find integers x, y, and z such that

$$X^n + Y^n = Z^n$$

In the margin of one book Fermat wrote "I have found for this a truly wonderful proof, but the margin is too small to hold it." In 1954, with the help of much prior work by outstanding mathematicians and the use of an electronic calculating machine, it was found that the theorem holds true for all exponents less than 2000, but this is certainly not a final proof. Fermat laid a foundation for the differential calculus, and independently of Descartes, discovered the principles of analytic geometry. A priority dispute ensued but it was peacefully settled due to Fermat's tact, courtesy, and friendly personality. He has been called the greatest French mathematician of the seventeenth century.

Probability Becomes a Science

In order to comprehend a discussion of the development of probability as a science, a simple definition must first be stated. You will have noted that in stating the probability of events thus far, we have said that the probability of throwing a certain number on a die in one toss is $1/6$; that the probability of throwing a tail on one toss of a coin is $1/2$; and in every example thus far shown the probability of the event has been stated as some fraction less than one, but greater than zero. The reader, having noted this, may well come to the following, correct conclusion: If the probability of an event is zero, it is certain that the event will *not* happen; if the probability is one the event is certain to happen; and if the probability is some fraction between zero and one, the larger the fraction the greater the chance that the event will happen. In terms of probability, then, zero may be defined as certainty that an event *will not* happen, and one may be defined as certainty that an event *will* happen.

We shall now turn to a consideration of the correspondence between Fermat and Pascal which forms the beginning of probability as a science, even though earlier work has been done in the field by Cardan, Galileo, and others. The correspondence began about 1654 with the famous "Problem of Points," a problem with which Cardan had been familiar. Pascal corresponded with Fermat concerning its solution, and both came up with the correct answer, but with different approaches.

Problems of this type deal with two players of equal skill who wish to stop playing a game before it is finished. If the number of points required to win, as well as the respective scores when they stop, are known, in what proportion should the stakes be divided? Basically the problem asks what probability each player has, at any stage of the game, of winning.

The following analysis of one such problem illustrates Pascal's method of reasoning: Assume two players play a game which requires three points to win and that each player has put up thirty-two pistoles (a former gold coin of Spain, worth about $4.00). Suppose that when they wish to cease play the first player has two points while the other has one. If they continued to play for one more point, the second player could either lose or tie the game. In either case the first player is assured of at least thirty-two pistoles so the remaining thirty-two should be split evenly, the first player taking forty-eight and the second sixteen.

Next, suppose the first player has two points and the second none. On the next trial the first player could either win or they would be in the same position as described in the previous paragraph. Therefore, the first player should have the forty-eight pistoles plus half of what is left, or a total of fifty-six pistoles; the second player then has eight pistoles.

Finally, suppose the first player has one point and the second none. If they play for an additional point, they would either be tied, or in the position just described. If tied, the first player is assured of thirty-two pistoles. In addition, he is entitled to half the difference between thirty-two and the fifty-six pistoles he would receive if he had two points and the second player none. This gives an additional twelve pistoles. Thus, the first player should have a total of forty-four pistoles and the second twenty pistoles. The division is seen to be in the ratio of eleven to five.

Fermat's solution to the "Problem of Points" depends on the theory of permutations as follows: Assume A has one point and B has none, that is, A needs two points to win and B needs three. Certainly the game will be decided in not more than four trials. Let a and b represent a win by A and B respectively. There are a total of sixteen permutations of a and b possible (*aaaa, aaab, aaba, aabb, abaa, abab, abba, abbb, baaa, baab, baba, babb, bbaa, bbab, bbba, bbbb*). As will be noted, there are eleven cases favorable to A, i.e., where a occurs at least twice; but only five cases favorable to B, that is, where b occurs three times or more. Since these are assumed to be equally likely, A's chance is to B's chance as eleven is to five. This agrees with Pascal's solution.

Another letter from Fermat to Pascal relates to a question which Pascal had proposed to Fermat: "A person undertakes to throw a six with a die in eight throws; supposing him to have made three throws without success, what portion of the stake should he be allowed to take on condition of giving up his fourth throw?" The chance of throwing a six is $1/6$ so that he should be allowed to take $1/6$ of the stake if he gives up his throw. But suppose we wish to estimate the value of the fourth throw before any throw is made. The first throw is worth $1/6$ of the stake; the second $1/6$ of that remaining, or $5/36$; the third $1/6$ of the remaining, or $25/216$; and the fourth $1/6$ of what now remains, or $125/1296$ of the stake. The "Problem of Points" and similar questions were discussed in great detail by Pascal and Fermat, but by no means did they exhaust all the possibilities. They confined themselves to the case in which the players were assumed to have equal skill; their methods would have been extremely laborious if applied to more complicated examples. Pascal often attempted short cuts and sometimes made mistakes while Fermat tended to be more thorough.

Games of chance are probably as old as the human desire to get something for nothing. Pascal and Fermat attempted to reduce unknown chances to laws. The mathematics of chance is the basis of our statistical analysis of the stock market, intelligence tests, insurance, biology, and much of modern mathematical physics, to mention only a few applications.

It would have been difficult to find two men better qualified for the title of founders of probability than Pascal and Fermat. However, systematic treatises on the subject came some half century after their work. Books on modern probability theory are often highly technical, yet the basic material found in the correspondence between Fermat and Pascal is often encountered in the introductory portion of such books.

Huygens: Probability in Print

Christian Huygens (also Hugens or Huyghens, 1629–1695, Dutch) is chiefly known for his work in physics, but he was also an able mathematician and astronomer. He was born at The Hague. He was the first to see that the pendulum could be used to regulate the movement of clocks, and he is credited with the construction of the first accurate timepiece. This he used, as planned, for measuring time in his astronomical work.

During one period of his life he helped shape the work of Leibniz. These two illustrious men met in Paris, and Huygens presented Leibniz with a copy of his work on the pendulum. Leibniz was greatly impressed with the ideas and begged Huygens to give him lessons on the subject. Huygens noted that Leibniz would be an apt student, so readily consented.

The versatile Huygens heard of the correspondence between Pascal and Fermat and ventured into this new field of probability. About 1657 (authorities differ as to the exact date) he published a treatise on probability, *De Ratiociniis in Ludo*

Aleae. This was the first printed on the subject of games of chance as Cardan's book did not appear in print until 1663. The book was partially responsible for stimulating Jacob Bernoulli, Montmort, and De Moivre. Huygens included simple cases of "Problems of Points" plus others relating to dice. At the end are listed five additional problems, without solutions, for the reader. Inasmuch as Jacob Bernoulli reprinted Huygen's treatise as the first of four parts of his *Ars Conjectandi*, together with a more detailed treatment of the work as a whole, further discussion will be deferred until later.

The concept of "mathematical expectation" is credited to Huygens. You will recall that this was discussed in Chapter 1 and is the product of the probability that an event will happen times the amount the player will receive if he wins. Mathematical expectation is not restricted to winnings, but may be applied to the value of any event. As an example if one wanted the mathematical expectation of the number of spots which would turn up when one die was tossed this could be computed as follows:

$$1(1/6) + 2(1/6) + 3(1/6) + 4(1/6) + 5(1/6) + 6(1/6) = 3.5$$

Huygens demonstrated that if the probability of a person winning a sum a is p and if the probability that he would win a sum b is q, then he may expect to win the total of $ap + bq$.

Huygens also wrote on the shape of many geometric curves. It is interesting to note that even though he was aware of the power of the "new" analytical geometry and the fundamentals of the calculus, he continued to write and show proofs almost entirely by the ancient Greek methods. He died at the age of sixty-six in the city of his birth.

In the next chapter we shall find that many of the well-known mathematicians of the period were beginning to take an interest in the subject of probability.

4

The Dabbler and the Antagonist

Although neither Leibniz nor Wallis did anything strikingly original in the field of probability, they did write on the subject, showing that they were aware of and concerned with it. These were two of the most distinguished mathematicians in their time, and it seems they felt this new topic was of sufficient importance to merit their attention.

Leibniz: The Dabbler

Gottfried Wilhelm Leibniz (also Leibnitz, 1646–1716, German) dabbled in many fields but seemed to master them all. He has been called a universal genius and made outstanding contributions to law, religion, philosophy, literature, logic, and mathematics. In fact his work in each of these fields was enough to complete any ordinary life. His father died when he was six, but by this time Leibniz had already developed an avid interest in history. He did much reading on his own, and at twelve had taught himself to read Latin and had begun the study of Greek. At fifteen he entered the University of Leipzig as a student of law, but because this did not occupy all his time he read on numerous other subjects. At the age of twenty he was fully qualified to receive the doctorate but the faculty refused to grant it. Supposedly this was because of his youth, but many felt that they were jealous of the fact that he knew more law than all of them put together.

In 1666 he published *Dissertatio de Arte Combinatoria* which is the earliest of his works connected with mathematics. Although the major portion of this work is filled with his ideas on philosophy and logic, he does construct a table similar to Pascal's triangle and then shows how to find the number of combinations of a certain set of items taken two, three, and four at a time. His formula for the number of combinations of n items taken two at a time was correct. In modern notation the formula is

$$C(n,2) = \frac{n!}{2! \, (n-2)!}$$

($n!$ is called n factorial and is defined as the product of the first n positive integers, for example, $3! = 3 \times 2 \times 1$). An interesting theorem given by him states: If n is a prime, the number of combinations of n things taken r at a time is divisible by n. A prime number you will recall is a number which is divisible only by itself and one. The first few primes are 2, 3, 5, 7, 11, 13, 17, 19, 23. Suppose we have nineteen items taken fifteen at a time. From Leibniz' formula we may write:

$$C(n,r) = \frac{n!}{r!(n-r)!}$$

In the specific case just mentioned we have

$$C(19,15) = \frac{19!}{15!4!} = 19 \times 17 \times 12 = 3876$$

which is divisible by nineteen.

Although Leibniz took a great interest in probability many of his contributions were not of as high a caliber as those of Pascal and Fermat. The concept of mathematical expectation was familiar to him. He proposed an application of this principle to law as follows: Of two individuals having claim to a sum of money, if the claim of the one is twice as likely to succeed as the other, the sum should be divided between them in that proportion. This suggestion, based on probability, seems sensible, although it is doubtful that it has ever been acted upon.

An essay of Leibniz' on the study of law led to his appointment to a commission for the revision of some statutes. He subsequently entered the diplomatic service and was invited to Paris in 1672. This was indeed a fortunate trip for him because it was there that he met Huygens and higher mathematics. As was mentioned earlier, he became a student of Huygens. By this time Leibniz had already invented a calculating machine which would not only add and subtract but would also multiply, divide, and extract roots.

In 1676 he was appointed court librarian and privy councilor to the Duke of Brunswick, and as the remaining forty years of his life were not particularly burdensome, he had time for other things. He read, wrote, and thought endlessly. The many references to which he calls attention in his writings is an indication of his vast reading. It is said that a lifelong characteristic of Leibniz was that he could work anywhere, any time, and under any conditions.

One of his discoveries, which is sometimes credited to James Gregory, 1638–1675, was

$$\pi/4 = 1 - 1/3 + 1/5 - 1/7 + 1/9 - 1/11 + - \cdots$$

This is not a very convenient way to compute π but is an interesting relationship connecting all the odd integers.

The last seven years of his life were embittered by a dispute with Newton. Fundamentally the question was over the invention of the calculus. The consensus now is that both of them independently invented it. Leibniz definitely had a better notational system in calculus and in other mathematical fields. He experimented with many symbols to see which was more advantageous. He used $+$, $-$, and $=$ in the modern sense, but primarily used $\frown$ for multiplication and $\smile$ for division.

Leibniz died in 1716 and it is said that only his faithful secretary attended his funeral.

Wallis: The Antagonist

John Wallis (1616–1703, English) thrived on disputes and had a very quarrelsome personality, although he was reported to be brilliant and witty in controversy. There was a long profitless quarrel with Thomas Hobbes which lasted over twenty-five years. Hobbes' mathematical work did not compare with Wallis', so Wallis could not hope to gain anything in winning. It is said that no man ever scorned personal popularity more completely, and he almost never admitted that he was in error. He had a hatred for compromise and was usually unwilling to listen to or try to understand his opponent's point of view. He took great issue with all French mathematicians, particularly Descartes, and seemed to feel that his own honor was at stake any time England was not given credit for a mathematical advance.

Wallis knew nothing about mathematics until his fifteenth year. It is reported that he picked up a mathematics book belonging to his brother and was so fascinated and entranced by the various signs and symbols that he had mastered the contents within two weeks. As fate would have it, he went to Cambridge intending to become a physician, even though his chief interest was in mathematics, but ended up being a clergyman and was made chaplain to Charles II in 1660.

After his maturity there was scarcely a year in which Wallis did not make a scholarly contribution to the world of learning. These contributions were not limited to mathematics, but in that field, unlike many other mathematicians of his day, he coordinated and extended what was known. He used the experimental approach many times, as did Galileo, but could not resist the temptation to show great contempt for Galileo's work. His enthusiasm and personal activities inspired others. His writings were on botany, music, and many other subjects as well as mathematics. He introduced our present symbol for infinity (∞) and was one of the founders of the Royal Society.

In his seventieth year he decided his energies should be exerted in the direction of algebra. His *Algebra* was published in 1685, with a *Discourse of Combinations, Alternations, and Aliquot Parts* attached to the end. This text contains the first serious attempt in England to write on the history of mathematics, and contains, as is noted from its title, a study into the subject of permutations and combinations. In the first chapter he shows an array of numbers similar to Pascal's triangle, but his style is clumsy and compares unfavorably with what has been called "the clear bright stream of thought" by Pascal. In the second chapter he gives examples of permutations and shows that given four letters, a, b, c, and d, if they are taken together there are $4 \times 3 \times 2 \times 1$ different ways to display them. He then exhibits the twenty-four permutations of these letters. He further forms the product of the first twenty-four integers. This is the number of permutations of twenty-four objects all taken together. He shows that the word *Messes* may only be displayed in sixty ways since the letter *e* appears twice and the letter *s* three times.

The interested student may wish to check the reasoning by use of formulas for permutations. For the number of permutations of *n* items taken *r* at a time the formula is

$$P(n,r) = n!/(n - r)!$$

For the number of permutations of *n* objects taken *n* at a time we then have

$$P(n,n) = n!/0! = n! \qquad \text{(0! is defined to be 1)}$$

For each duplicate, for example one item is repeated *k* times and another repeated *m* times, it is then necessary to divide by *k*! and *m*! respectively to obtain the number of *distinct* permutations. In the case of the word *Messes*, the number of distinct permutations is computed as

$$P(6,6) = 6!/0!3!2! = 60.$$

In comparing the formulas for permutations and combinations, it is seen that in general there are *r*! more permutations than combinations, the formula for the number of combinations of *n* objects taken *r* at a time being

$$C(n,r) = n!/r!(n - r)!$$

In the final chapter of *Algebra*, Wallis shows solutions of two problems which Fermat had proposed as a challenge. It appears that Fermat's theory of numbers had a much greater influence on Wallis than did Pascal's theory of probability.

Until the twilight of his life he persisted in many animosities, and his memory never failed him. On various sleepless nights he did mathematical problems in his head. On one occasion he supposedly extracted the square root of a fifty-three digit number, giving the correct answer to twenty-seven figures, without aid of pen or paper.

It will be noted that the mathematicians whose contributions to the field of probability have been discussed found themselves primarily, although not exclusively, working with problems involving games of chance. While it is true that this formed a very fruitful beginning for the subject, it is also true that probability has many other valuable uses. It may be worthwhile to turn our attention to some work which was developing in the application of probability to fields other than dice, card games, and the like. Some of these aspects will be considered in the next chapter.

5

The Odds of Life

From time immemorial man has been concerned with the length of his own life as well as the lives of his loved ones. No one has ever found a mathematical formula by which to calculate the length of a specific life; nevertheless life insurance companies must have some method of determining your life span. How does an insurance company determine the premium on a life insurance policy, or the premium for fire insurance, or insurance on an automobile? Each holiday the National Safety Council predicts the number of accidental deaths which will occur. On what basis do they determine these figures which are often so accurate? The very heart of this problem is attacked from the standpoint of probability and statistics.

Graunt: Captain of Statistics

John Graunt (1620–1674, English) is said to have founded statistics. It is to this man that we owe our first attempt to interpret mass biological phenomena and social behavior from numerical data. In his early life he was a merchant of small wares as well as an army captain. His success in these pursuits gave him leisure time to indulge in other interests.

Graunt had become interested in the weekly listings of births and deaths and the result was his book, *Natural and Political Observations made upon the Bills of Mortality*. Its original purpose was to report the progress of the plague, but he further conceived the value of determining the growth of the population. Studies of the plague might show where it was increasing or decreasing, so the rich could move to another location and thus avoid it. Studies of population growth could help the tradesman judge the size and type of the group with which he would more likely have dealings. Charles II was so pleased with the book that he proposed Graunt's name for membership in the Royal Society. He was duly elected.

Since no mathematical formula will tell whether a specified individual will be alive at the end of any given period of time, no company could afford to offer life insurance to a single person except at a prohibitive charge. However, tables are available showing the deaths which occur year by year in a large group of individuals. These are known as mortality tables. Such tables make it possible to apply the principles of probability to the field of life insurance. If it is known that of ten thousand men alive on their nineteenth birthday, twenty-four will not live until their twentieth birthday, we may say that the probability of dying during the year is 24/10,000. This concept of probability, determined by past record or by experiment, as contrasted with counting the logical possibilities of success or failure, is called *empirical, experimental,* or *statistical,* as was noted in Chapter 1. Results in the past are used to predict events yet to happen, assuming there has been no appreciable change in the circumstances.

While no company would dare to issue a single life insurance policy of $1000 for one year to a man aged nineteen for a charge of $2.40, if ten thousand such policies could be issued, the income would be $24,000. The use of empirical probability would indicate that on the average twenty-four claims would be paid during the year, resulting in a payment of $24,000. The company would be unlikely to have the loss of a major sum of money. To provide a margin of safety and to cover the company's cost of doing business the charge would no doubt be made appreciably more than $2.40. Nevertheless we have here the fundamental concept of life insurance, based on the use of empirical probability. The details of determining how large a margin of safety is needed, providing insurance for a period longer than one year, and making provision such that the charge will not become prohibitive in old age, together with other features, can be found in many texts.

Fundamentally, life insurance pays upon the death of the individual. Therefore, the insuring company is interested in your chance to die. Contrasted with this is the concept of a life annuity in which, starting at a specified age, a company agrees to pay to an individual a yearly sum as long as the individual is living. Now we find the idea of the empirical probability of living is developed from mortality tables obtained from a large group of people. The insuring company is here interested in your chance to live. It follows that in either life insurance or life annuity calculations, statistics and probability are basic.

De Witt: The Legislator

John De Witt (1625–1672, Dutch) devoted considerable time to mathematics, although he was primarily a statesman and was quite involved in internal strife. He did research on annuities and was one of the first to make a careful study of them. They had been in existence since Roman times but there had been very little theory developed. He was aware of the correspondence between Pascal and Fermat, but his purpose in writing was to attack the problem from a practical rather than a theoretical or gambling point of view. He was primarily concerned with life annuities as they might affect public finance and only secondarily with people who might wish to secure for themselves a living in their old age.

Some of the reasoning used by De Witt would seem very crude by present day standards. In the analysis of one problem he considers a life annuity, but assumes no one would live beyond the age of seventy-five or seventy-six. This is an interesting commentary on the life expectancy of a man at that time. Lacking adequate mortality tables he more or less arbitrarily assumes that the probability of living is equal throughout each of the first fifty years; in the next ten years it is two-thirds of what it was before; in the next ten years one-half, and in the last seven years of life one-third of what it was during the first fifty years. The table he used for a portion of his calculations is nothing more than what we know as Pascal's triangle.

De Witt became the Great Pensionary of the province of

Holland. As a result of the various political intrigues in which
he was involved Cornelis, his brother, was arrested on a
charge of conspiracy and sentenced to banishment. John went
to see him shortly before his release. A mob broke into the
jail and lynched both men. Thus the life of a great statesman
and budding mathematician was snuffed out by the ignorance
of mob rule. In view of his deep involvement in the affairs of
state it is commendable that he contributed so much to the
study of life annuities. It does seem rather unusual that the
underlying theory of such an important subject should not
have been discussed until this time.

Halley: The Benefactor

Edmund Halley (1656–1742, English) published the first
complete mortality tables for various ages. These are often
said to be the real beginning of the theory of annuities. The
tables previously published had not been constructed in a
very scientific manner. Halley's tables furnished a foundation
for all later works of this kind, in fact he has been called the
inventor of mortality tables.

Halley was born of wealthy parents, who indulged him in
every advantage, including an excellent education. He early
showed an interest in mathematics and astronomy. His interest
in the problem of gravity prompted him to visit Newton.
This was fortunate because through Halley's encouragement
and financial assistance Newton was able to publish his famous
Principia.

One of Halley's greatest achievements was his study of the
orbits of comets. He predicted one comet to have a period of
seventy-six years and on Christmas Day in 1758 the conjecture
was verified. It has since been known as Halley's comet and
returned in 1835 and 1910. He died at the age of eighty-six,
and has been described as generous, easy-going, free from
jealousy, and a man who enjoyed his life and work in general.

In his mortality tables he showed, of one thousand alive at
age one year, how many were still alive at two, three, four,
and so on. His explanations of how to use such a table are

essentially the same as those found at the present time in introductory works on the subject. For example, he asks how to find the probability, although Halley calls it "Odds," that a person will not die before attaining a proposed age. After stating the general method, Halley illustrates by finding the odds that a man of forty will live seven more years. From his table, of 445 persons alive at 40 years, 377 are still living at 47. Hence, as we have seen, the probability of a man living at 40 to be still alive at 47 is 377/445. Halley considered the problem in this manner: 377 persons will be still alive at 47, while 68 will have died. The *odds* in favor of living are 377 to 68, or roughly 5½ to 1.

The concept of *odds* in favor of an event has often been used. Unfortunately, the two ways of consideration of probability are often confused. For example, from a suit of 13 cards, the *probability* of drawing a face card is 3/13. There are three face cards and ten non-face cards. The *odds* in favor of drawing a face card are three to ten and *not* three to thirteen. It is perhaps unfortunate that these two essentially equivalent concepts have been used, for confusion sometimes results.

In another example Halley asked at what number of years there is an even chance that a person of any age shall die. In his example he uses a person of age thirty; from the table the number living at that age is 531, half of which is 265. Halley finds this number of persons living to lie between 57 and 58 years. Hence a man of thirty may reasonably expect, he says, to live between 27 and 28 years.

Halley also discusses the evaluation of annuities covering two or more persons, which we would now call joint annuities. Although the number of persons involved in his tables is very much smaller than that used in mortality tables at the present time, the fundamental principles are identical. For some reason in the development of certain underlying theory he uses a geometrical approach whereas an algebraic treatment would seem to have been more simple.

Although several of the men we have considered up to this time made very significant contributions to probability, the subject was often of minor interest to them and occupied a relatively small portion of their time. In the next chapter we find men who devoted large portions of their time to this subject.

6

The Brothers Bernoulli

Mighty Mathematical Minds

At the approach of the eighteenth century, men of great ability began dedicating large amounts of time and effort to the subject of probability. The Bernoulli family's contributions to probability may be compared to the Bach family's contributions to music. Within one hundred years at least nine members of the family made remarkable contributions to mathematics and physics. Four obtained honors from the Paris Academy of Science. It seemed to be a family trait to start out in one profession, usually law or medicine, and finally turn to mathematics or physics. Originally a Protestant family from Antwerp, Belgium, they were driven out in the latter 1500's by religious persecution. They stopped first in Frankfurt and then in a few years moved to Basel in Switzerland. Belgium did not know what fame this family could have brought her.

Since the last part of the seventeenth century members of the family were found in universities either teaching or doing research in the fields of mathematics and physics. About half of the descendants were what we would now classify as gifted and the others were above average in ability. Probably the most famous of the clan were the brothers Jacob I and Johannes I (Jacques and Jean).

The Bernoulli's

Jacob Bernoulli (or Jacques, 1654–1705, Swiss) was born in the same year that Pascal and Fermat were corresponding on the "Problem of Points." His father forbade him to study mathematics or astronomy in the hope that he would turn to theology, but such was not to be the case. Jacob became interested in the calculus, and after mastering it himself without a teacher, was one of the first to make its study popular on the continent. He traveled widely and met Leibniz and other mathematicians. He served as professor of mathematics at Basel. His writings were on many topics, but we are primarily concerned with his book *Ars Conjectandi*. This was the first book devoted wholly to the subject of probability as well as the first treating probability as a separate branch of mathematics. It was also the best attempt up to that time to place the theory of probability on a sound mathematical foundation. Orginally it was planned to consist of four parts. The first was a reprint of certain problems proposed by Huygens. The second was a thorough treatment of permutations and combinations. Parts of this section are quite modern in style and would fit into current discussion of the subject. The third part gave the solutions to various problems arising out of games of chance, and the final part dealt with applications of the theory of probability to civil, moral, and economic questions. It has been said that nearly every algebra book since the time of Jacob Bernoulli has included some work on probability. This statement is not absolutely correct, but it does indicate the importance which probability has assumed in the last 250 years. *Ars Conjectandi* was published posthumously in 1713 and was edited by Nicolaus Bernoulli II, who also made contributions to the theory of probability. In the preface Nicolaus states that he does not feel competent to complete or revise the work of his uncle, so the work remains essentially unchanged, with the fourth part unfinished. Much of the work is highly technical; his solution to the "Problem of Points" is extended to players of unequal skill.

One of the first problems discussed relates to a game played with two dice. The first player has one throw and the second two throws, then the first player has two throws and the second three throws, and so on until one player wins. The first player will win provided he throws a six before the second player throws a seven. If the second player produces a seven before the first player throws a six, the second player is the winner. Bernoulli shows that the chance of the first player

winning as contrasted with that of the second player is in the
ratio 10,355 to 12,276. There are many problems of a similar
type.

Bernoulli discusses at some length the question of the possible throws which can be made with two or more dice. Earlier
writers had tabulated the results for two dice and had studied
the question of three dice, but Bernoulli extended the discussion to any number of dice. Essentially he reached the conclusion of a theorem which in modern notation could be stated:
The number of ways in which a total of m points can be obtained by throwing n dice at once is equal to the coefficient of
x^m in the expansion of $(x + x^2 + x^3 + x^4 + x^5 + x^6)^n$.

The final part, although left incomplete, is considered by
many the most important portion. Perhaps the most outstanding topic is the statement and investigation of what is now
known as Bernoulli's theorem. There have been many ways of
phrasing the theorem. Two alternative statements will be
given, although neither is in all respects mathematically rigor-
ous: (1) If an event has a probability p of succeeding and if
the number of trials made is infinite, the proportion of successes will certainly be p; (2) If an event has a probability p
of succeeding, as the number of trials n of the event becomes
extremely large the ratio of the number of successes to np will
approach unity. Even though these statements may make the
theorem seem relatively simple, the proof involves many difficulties and is quite lengthy. Bernoulli states that he devoted
some twenty years to it. Details can be found in advanced
references.

Some of the letters exchanged between the Bernoullis and
others bristled with emotion. However, if individuals lose their
temper over a bridge game, politics, and other topics, why
should they not become almost violent in the discussion of the
infinitely more exciting problems of mathematics?

Nicolaus Bernoulli II (1687–1759), the editor of his uncle's
book on probability, applied the subject to various questions,
particularly those relating to the probability of human life. In
doing this he used a somewhat crude table which we would
now call a mortality table and which his Uncle Jacob had de-

veloped from a study of vital statistics. Nicolaus applied the
theory of probability to the following questions: the length of
time required to assume a man dead who has vanished and
has not been heard from; the value of a life annuity; problems
of lotteries; marine insurance; and the sum which should be
set aside at a child's birth to assure the payment of a specified
amount when the child reaches some given age. One application to law is his attempt to estimate the probability that an
accused person is innocent. He assumes that any single witness
testifying against the accused is twice as likely to be lying as
telling the truth. But if several testify against the accused, the
question of the probability of his innocence requires much
more careful analysis, which Bernoulli carries out.

Johannes Bernoulli I (or Jean, 1667–1748) seems to be more
intimately connected with Jacob I than were some of the other
Bernoullis. Jacob was his teacher for a time, but they were
anything but congenial. Johannes' father insisted that this son
should become a merchant, but Johannes devoted his time
first to medicine and then became interested in mathematics.
His discoveries were many and usually independent. He has
been described as violent, abusive, jealous, and at times dis-
honest. He had more varied interests than his brother Jacob,
making contributions to physics, chemistry, and astronomy as
well as mathematics.

Apparently not having learned anything from disobeying his
own father in turning toward science, Johannes insisted that
his son Daniel not follow mathematical pursuits. This insist-
ence took the form of cruel mistreatment of the child in an
apparent attempt to destroy his self-confidence and later tried
to force him into business. With a Bernoulli nothing but
science would suffice. Apparently Johannes and Daniel both
competed for a prize from the French Academy of Science.
The father did not win the prize, the son did. The father's
reaction was to throw the son out of his house.

The contributions of Johannes were said to have been almost as numerous as his controversies. He hated Newton and
underestimated his ability. He seems, however, to have been
a successful teacher and inspired his pupils with the same

deep interest in mathematics that he himself held. It is reported that his physical and intellectual vigor remained intact until his death at the age of eighty.

Daniel Bernoulli (1700-1782, Swiss) added much worthwhile material to the field of probability. Nicolaus, his older brother, gave him lessons in geometry at the age of eleven. In spite of the fact that he studied medicine and became a physician, at the age of twenty-five he accepted an appointment as professor of mathematics at St. Petersburg. In 1733 he returned to Basel as professor of anatomy, botany, and later, physics. His work was of a very high caliber. He won or shared in at least ten prizes put up by the French Academy, including the one which resulted in his expulsion from his father's house.

At one time he met a stranger and introduced himself as Daniel Bernoulli. The stranger, not believing he was meeting such a famous man, replied sarcastically, "and I am Isaac Newton." Bernoulli considered this one of the most sincere compliments he ever received.

Daniel has been called the founder of mathematical physics. His investigations in probability were also remarkable for their boldness and originality. One of the more famous problems in probability which he discussed is known as the "Petersburg Problem" or the "Petersburg Paradox." Many outstanding mathematicians have discussed, with various explanations, this particular problem. Suppose we consider a game in which the player tosses an honest coin. If he gets a head on the first toss the banker pays him $2. If the head does not appear until the second toss the player receives $4; if it does not appear until the third toss he wins $8; if the head does not appear until the kth toss, the player wins 2^k dollars. The question is: What is the mathematical expectation of the player? Or, to state it another way: What can a player afford to pay for the privilege of engaging in this game? The probability of winning on the first toss is 1/2; the amount won would be $2; therefore, the mathematical expectation is (1/2) ($2) or $1. In order for the win to occur on the second toss, the player must throw tails on the first toss (probability =

1/2). The amount won would be $4; the mathematical expec-
tation would be $(1/2)(1/2)(\$4)$ or $1. Hence the mathematical
expectation of winning on *either* the first or the second toss is
$1 + $1 or $2. In like manner the mathematical expectation of
winning on the third toss is $1. Although it is not very likely
to happen, it is by no means impossible that the first nine
tosses yield tails, and the player wins on the tenth toss. Reasoning as before, the mathematical expectation of a win on
the tenth toss is $1, and the mathematical expectation of win-
ning on the first, or the second, or the third, . . . , or the tenth
toss is $1 + $1 + $1 + . . . + $1 or $10. If it is agreed that the
game is to terminate with ten tosses, the player could pay $10
to play the game, and in the long run he would neither win
nor lose any appreciable sum of money. However, if the game
is to go on indefinitely, the mathematical expectation becomes
$1 + $1 + . . . , a never ending sequence, whose sum becomes
infinite, that is, greater than any figure which may be named.
Hence the player should pay an infinite sum of money to
participate. Obviously, no player could fulfill such a condition,
and even if he could pay an enormous sum, the proposition
would be far from a bargain. Herein lies the paradox. In an
attempt to explain the paradox Daniel Bernoulli pointed out
the desirability of receiving different sums of money is not
directly proportional to the size of the sum. One suggestion
has been made that the winning of any sum larger than 2^{24}
dollars ($16,777,216) is "morally equal" to winning 2^{24} dollars;
meaning that $16,777,216 is already so great a figure that any
additional winnings would be insignificant. This led to Bernoulli's concept of *moral expectation* as contrasted with *mathematical expectation*. This is not an entirely satisfactory solution of the "Petersburg Paradox" but it is the first instance
known of an attempt to take into account a concept known to
modern students of economics as the diminishing marginal
utility of money. The "Petersburg Paradox" further indicates
the difficulties which may be encountered as one advances
into more complex topics in probability.

Daniel was a prolific writer. He showed how calculus could
be used in the theory of probability. He used probability to

determine the number of survivors at a given age from a given number of births; to determine the mortality due to smallpox at various stages of life; and to determine how much inoculation lengthens life. Thus probability was applied to medicine, smallpox in particular, which was then a deadly killer. Perhaps at the present time we would be more likely to find the applications to some other unconquered dread disease. In recent years we have seen statistics and probability applied to the question of whether or not cigarette smoking causes cancer.

Montmort: The Popularizer

Pierre Raymond de Montmort (1678–1719, French) attained some prominence during this period, partly because of his writings and partly because of his correspondence about and with the Bernoulli family. He did some writing on other subjects, but his main work was on the theory of probability. He gave a general solution of the "Problem of Points." Although his *Essai d'Analyse sur les Jeux de Hazards* was said to be intended more for mathematicians than for professional gamesters, the book enjoyed wide popularity. The first part concerns the theory of combinations; the second part discusses games of chance which depend on cards; the third part treats games which depend on dice; the fourth part discusses various problems, including the five problems which Huygens left for his readers to solve.

It appears that Montmort became interested in this field when some friends requested him to analyze the advantage of the banker in a certain gambling game. Montmort regretted that Bernoulli was unable to complete his work and was conceited enough to feel his writings could make up for some of the missing material. In his work he makes brief reference to Huygens, Pascal, and Fermat.

Some of his material was a distinct novelty. One particular problem may be worthy of mention: Suppose we remove the hat checks from all hats in a cloakroom and then distribute them at random to the guests. If any guest receives his own hat we will say that this forms a "match." If there are ten guests what is the probability that there is at least one "match"? How does this compare with the probability at a gathering where there are 1,000 people present? Surprisingly, the probability is essentially independent of the number of people involved; it is roughly 2/3 in either of the cases mentioned, or for that matter, for any number of guests. The proof is beyond the scope of this book. Montmort's death at the age of forty-one was due to the dreaded disease smallpox.

7

Calculating the Risk

De Moivre: The Refugee

At first glance it might seem that a person living at the same time as the Bernoulli family would have no chance to add anything outstanding in probability, but such was not the case. The eighteenth century, which opened with intense mathematical activity, continued unabated in many diverse directions under a host of different men. One of these individuals, whose name has appeared in previous chapters, was *Abraham De Moivre* (1667–1754, English) who was of French descent, but he and his family were forced to leave France when he was eighteen because of the revocation of the Edict of Nantes. His education and friends were among the English so he is generally considered to be an English mathematician. It is reported that his mathematical education started when he accidentally came upon Newton's *Principia* while he was tutoring for a living. He was confident that all he would have to do would be to pick up the book and read it. He soon found that the material was beyond his immediate comprehension. He had so few leisure hours that he tore out a few pages at a time, stuck them in his pocket and took them with him. Thus he could study between tutoring jobs. He later became a fellow of the Royal Society and thus was intimately acquainted with Newton, Halley, and others. It is said that when Newton was asked questions about his *Principia* he would suggest that the individuals go to Mr. De Moivre for the answers.

De Moivre is best remembered for his work in probability, annuities, and trigonometry. In addition to publishing several articles he wrote two outstanding works: *Doctrine of Chances* (1718) and *Miscellanea Analytica* (1730).

De Moivre's work *Annuities upon Lives* played an important role in the history of mathematics of life insurance which
involves probability to a great extent. Such work is often
termed actuarial mathematics.

Of the many people to whom England has given some kind
of asylum, it would be hard to find one who gave her more
honor than did De Moivre. His work in probability surpassed
that of any one up to that time, and some authorities have
felt that he contributed more to this field than any single individual with the possible exception of Laplace. The fact that
he neglected to show some of his methods and proofs is indeed
unfortunate.

Possibly the solving of problems and puzzles attracted De
Moivre to the theory of probability which gained new impetus
under his able guidance. One treatise was contained in three
issues of the *Philosophical Transactions*. This was later expanded and published under the title of *Doctrine of Chances*
or a *Method of Calculating the Probabilities of Events in
Play* and was dedicated to Newton. Not only did these contain
many problems in probability but also much material on annuities. De Moivre discussed in some detail the following
fundamental theorem: If the odds for the success of an event
at a single trial are as a is to b, then the chance that the
event will happen at least r times in n trials is found by taking
the first $n - r + 1$ terms in the expansion of $(a + b)^n$ and
dividing this by $(a + b)^n$. (Note the use of "odds" rather than
the term "Probability of success.") As in many of his problems,
De Moivre gives his result without showing a formal method
of proof. In order to find the chance of an event happening
just r times he directed the reader to subtract the chance that
it will happen *at least* $r - 1$ times from the chance that it will
happen *at least* r times. As an example, voting age is 21,
meaning a voter must be 21 or over, that is, at least 21 years
of age. If we wanted to know the voters exactly 21 years old
we might find the number who are at least 21 and subtract
from this those who are over 21, that is, those at least 22.
Another approach could be made as follows: If p is the probability of the success of an event, and q the probability of its

failure, the probability of exactly r successes followed by $n - r$ failures is $p \times p \times p \times p \ldots$ (r times) multiplied by $q \times q \times q \times q \times \ldots$ ($n - r$ times). This could be written as $p^r q^{n-r}$. Since order is immaterial for a success, we must multiply this quantity by the total number of combinations possible. In many modern texts the formula

$$C(n,r)p^r q^{n-r}$$

is given for the probability that an event will happen *exactly* r times in n trials. De Moivre developed probability, then proceeded to problems involving permutations and combinations, whereas most texts now proceed from permutations and combinations to the theory of probability.

Another problem which De Moivre proposed discusses a game in which A has two chances to beat B while B has only one chance to beat A; however, there is also one chance which allows both to withdraw their own stake. The problem is to find the gain which A can make. The problem is not particularly difficult; De Moivre states it is included in order to warn beginners against the mistake of assuming that it is not necessary to consider the situation where both players may withdraw. The reader may be interested in attempting to show that A's probable gain is one-fourth of his stake.

On November 12, 1733 De Moivre presented a seven-page paper: *Approximatio ad Summam Terminorum Binomii $(a + b)^n$ in Seriem Expansi*. The paper was presented privately to some friends. This work, together with some other studies involving the binomial theorem led him to the idea of what we now call the *normal probability curve*. As a result, November 12, 1733 is usually taken as the date of the origin of this curve. In presenting the paper De Moivre was doubtful that the normal probability curve would be of much value except as it applied to certain games of chance—indeed a false hypothesis.

The curve can really only be adequately studied by some material obtained by the use of higher mathematics, in particular the calculus. However, following De Moivre, an approach may be made by use of the binomial theorem. If we toss three coins at once and if we represent a head by H and a tail by T the various possibilities are HHH, HHT, HTH, THH, HTT, THT, TTH, and TTT. If we are not interested in the order of occurrence these might be represented by HHH, 3 HHT, 3 HTT, and TTT; if we adopt the convention that HH may be written as H^2, while H^3T would mean three heads and one tail, the expansion of $(H + T)^n$ represents symbolically the various possibilities that can arise when n coins are tossed at once. Suppose we attempt to show such an expansion graphically. At equal distances along the horizontal scale the number of heads may be represented; the corresponding fre-

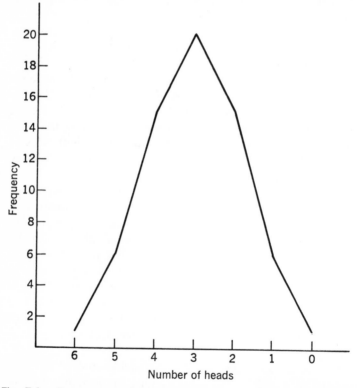

Fig. 7-1.   Frequency polygon. Since six coins were tossed, this polygon has six sides. The number of coins tossed and the number of sides in the polygon will always be equal.

quency of occurrence can be plotted along the vertical scale. Such a graph, for the case in which $n = 6$, is shown in Fig. 7-1.

A figure such as this is sometimes referred to as a frequency polygon or a probability polygon. With six coins we have a six-sided figure, with ten coins we would have a ten-sided figure, and so on. As the number of coins tossed is increased, the probability polygon has an increasing number of sides. As the number of sides increases the polygon approaches more and more closely the form of a smooth curve. A possible definition would be that as the number of sides, n, becomes infinitely large, the limiting position of the sides of the probability polygon is what is known as the *normal probability curve*, also called the normal curve, the Gaussian curve, the error curve, or the normal frequency curve.

At one time the normal curve was looked upon as a fundamental law, that is, it was believed that all distributions of quantitative data would be governed by the laws of probability applicable to this curve. We now know that this viewpoint is erroneous. This is particularly true in the fields of the social sciences and economics. The normal curve is only one of a large number of curves encountered in various situations; it is, however, one of the most important.

It will perhaps be of value to summarize certain of the general characteristics of the curve. Without any attempt at

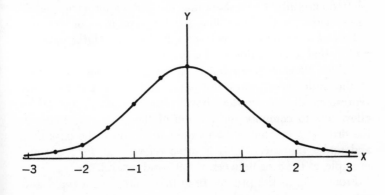

Fig. 7-2. The standard normal curve.

derivation it will be stated that the mathematical equation of such a curve can be written in several forms, one of which is

$$y = \frac{1}{\sqrt{2\pi}}\, e^{-\frac{1}{2}x^2}$$

This is often called the standard form of the normal curve. No attempt will here be made to give any interpretation to the meaning of x and y; they may at present merely be considered as abscissa and ordinate. A graph of the standard normal curve is shown in Fig. 7-2.

Study of the equation of the normal curve together with examination of the graph will show certain properties of the curve. In addition, tables of the normal curve obtained from its equation are available; consideration of such a table may make the results more obvious. It will be noted that positive and negative values of x yield the same value for y, in other words, the curve is symmetric with respect to the y-axis. The highest point on the curve is that for which the value of x is zero. The height of the curve continually decreases as we move away from the highest point, more and more rapidly for a time, then more slowly. Mathematically, the points where this change begins are known as points of inflection; they are found where $x = \pm 1$. There is no value of x which will make the height of the curve above the base line equal to zero. A graph may create the impression that this is not true, but if plotted carefully it will show that the curve approaches indefinitely close to the base line for large positive or negative values of x, though it never actually touches. Mathematically we say that the base line is an *asymptote*.

Tables likewise give what is called "area under the curve." If the entire area below the curve and above the base line represents all cases under consideration, or 100%, the tables allow one to compute the portion of the area lying between the ordinates erected at two values of x, above the base line, and under the curve. This is often referred to, for a specific example, as the area between $x = 0.5$ and $x = 1.2$.

From 1733 to the present time there has been a rapid and extensive use of the normal curve and now its applications are found in various fields which at first thought would seem unrelated. Since one approach to the derivation of the normal probability curve is from the viewpoint of the binomial expansion it is possible to reverse the reasoning and use the normal curve to approximate a situation involving the binomial expansion. With tables of the normal curve readily available this may avoid an almost prohibitively lengthy computation. As a single example suppose we wished to compute the probability of obtaining between 180 and 200 heads out of 500 tosses of a coin. Direct computation would require, as outlined earlier, the computation of a great many terms in the expansion of $(H + T)^{500}$; the approximation by use of the normal curve yields an answer with relatively little computation required. Details of the method of approximation are available in many texts on statistics or probability.

Many of the applications of the normal curve are independent of the binomial distribution. Many phenomena in widely scattered fields can best be described by use of the normal curve, in other words its use seems to preserve certain underlying characteristics of the data. Moreover the ever important problem of sampling is in many respects dependent upon the normal curve. Many of the results obtained from the study of samples are developed on assumptions based largely upon this curve. Although the normal curve is a theoretical one which may never appear exactly in an actual situation, it serves well as a "mathematical model" for many situations which do occur.

Many workers in the field of physical science have verified the fact that repeated observations of physical measurements are distributed in a manner dependent upon the normal curve; in particular the distribution of observed measurements about the average value shows that positive and negative deviations are about equally frequent, large deviations or errors are much less frequent than small deviations, and that extremely large errors or deviations are either very rare or do not occur. The causes of these errors or deviations may be numerous, but since each is as likely to increase as to decrease the error, and also since each is more likely to produce a small rather than a large error, we have justification for the normal curve, or as it is often called in this situation, the normal curve of error.

A practical application is found in artillery work where for a given setting on a target, shells may fall short or long because of the effect of various factors, such as slight variations in air pressure, temperature, quality of powder, size of the shell, wind, and so on. Again since these are operating according to the laws of chance, we will find the distribution of "shorts" and "longs" following the normal curve, extreme variations from the average point of impact being rare, "longs" and "shorts" appearing in essentially equal numbers. A similar situation arises with respect to the firing of long-range missiles. Although the amount of deviation may be greater than for an artillery shell, the fundamental pattern of distribution again is governed by the normal curve of error.

There are many other applications of the normal curve. We might ask, for example, what proportion of a group falls within specified limits or conversely what limits include a specified proportion. It has been found to hold true that certain physical measurements of adult individuals, such as height or weight, follow a pattern based on the normal curve. If information were available about the average height of senior high school men, including some information about the spread or variation of such heights, we could by use of the normal curve determine what proportion of such a group would fall between the heights of 5 feet 10 inches and 6 feet 1 inch. In like manner we could ask what heights should be selected so that students falling between these heights would include the middle 50 percent of the students.

An application is that of the classification of a group on the basis of ability. This problem is not restricted to teacher's marks but seems to carry so much interest for the student that it will be used for an illustration.

Many authorities in the field of education believe that teachers' marks or grades for a large number of unselected students should be distributed in accordance with the normal curve. There is a distinct doubt as to the validity of this conclusion if the group happens to be highly selected, as for example students electing a course in their major field, or a section of a large class which has already been divided on some measure of ability. Likewise by no means should it be implied that a normal distribution should be followed with small classes. However, with reasonably large groups of un-selected students over a period of years one may expect that the distribution of marks will approximate that obtained by applying the theory of the normal probability curve.

Let us therefore assume that the scores are available for a reasonably large and unselected group of students and that we wish to classify the group by assigning five marks, A, B, C, D, and F. On the assumption of a normal distribution we shall assume the range of ability for each mark is equal, then pro-ceed to determine the percentage which should receive each mark. But a real problem presents itself. We have seen that the normal curve extends indefinitely in both directions. This means that theoretically there is no limit to how large a score a student could receive nor is there any limit to how low a score he might make. Tables show that for such a distribution there is a very small percentage of the group who would have a score beyond the value $x = 3$ (details of converting actual scores into x values are here omitted). Such extreme cases at either end actually amount to less than one-fourth of one per-cent of the total group. Arbitrarily we agree to disregard this small portion of the group, and we restrict ourselves to a range of six units on the x scale, from $x = -3$ to $x = +3$. Each of the five letter marks will then cover a range of $1.2x$. Tables are so constructed that it is possible to obtain the percentage of the total group which lies between any two specified values of x. On this basis reference to such tables allows us to find the percentages required. We discover that we should assign 3½ percent A's, 24 percent B's, 45 percent C's, 24 percent D's, and 3½ percent F's.

If we examine the argument just presented we discover that more or less arbitrarily it was assumed that the total range was six units on the x scale. One might just as well argue that since a range of five units on the x scale would include in excess of 98½ percent of the total cases, the very few cases not included may well be unusual enough to merit special consideration. On this assumption the total range to be divided into five equal parts is $5x$, and each part will be of length x. Evaluation by use of tables shows that under this assumption we should assign approximately 7 percent A's, 24 percent B's, 38 percent C's, 24 percent D's, and 7 percent F's. This is the distribution which is usually suggested in teacher's class record books. One could argue with equal justification that the curve could be cut off at four or three and one-half x units on either side and then analyze the situation as just shown. It is now seen that the statement of grading *by the curve* needs considerable clarification. It is not the purpose of this discussion to argue for or against any or all of the assumptions mentioned but rather to point out the need for careful consideration of the problems involved.

It cannot be too strongly emphasized that conclusions drawn from the use of the normal curve are only valid if applied to distributions where assumptions of normality are at least approximately justified. At one time some individuals thought that all distributions were normal, but it is now known that there are many distributions which are not even approximately normal. Granted that the normal curve is of great importance, it does not add to accuracy to attempt to apply conclusions based on the standard normal curve to a situation where this procedure is completely unjustified.

Unfortunately students and some teachers have been encouraged in their belief that the normal curve involves a fundamental principle according to which all educational or psychological data are distributed. This has been emphasized by the fact that scores from many "standardized" educational and psychological tests form distributions which follow very nearly that suggested by the normal curve. The fact is often completely overlooked that the individuals constructing the test selected test items which would produce this very result. It is not intended to imply that this is incorrect but one must not draw the conclusion that because test scores are so distributed, the traits, abilities, or accomplishments that the tests are supposed to measure are likewise distributed.

In much of the theory of probability there is occasion to use factorials. We have previously noted that the product of the first n positive integers is called n factorial. It is customarily written $n!$ although for many years the symbol was $\lfloor n$. This change in notation is reported to have been at the request of printers; it being much simpler to print the new notation than the old. The calculation of factorials is not particularly difficult, at least for small numbers. We find that $3! = 1 \times 2 \times 3 = 6$ and that $5! = 5 \times 4 \times 3 \times 2 \times 1 = 120$. (It has been stated that a good test of mathematical ability is to define the concept of a factorial, then ask the person to estimate the size of $10!$. Before going farther, the reader may be interested in forming his estimate, then checking by actual calculation. A guess too small is far more the usual practice than is one too large; the larger the estimate, the better it is said is the mathematician.)

If there is occasion to use factorials for numbers of considerable size, perhaps in excess of 1000, we find the computation to be extremely laborious if not almost impossible. Tables are available for certain values. De Moivre presented one such table in which he gave 14-figure logarithms of factorials from $10!$ to $900!$ at intervals of ten units. Where tables are not available it is common to use an approximation for the value of factorials by Stirling's formula, but it seems in reality due to De Moivre.

No sketch of De Moivre would be complete without the following story, which may be hypothetical. Shortly before his death he announced that it was necessary for him to have fifteen minutes more sleep every day. As he was then getting six hours sleep each day, there would obviously be a limit to this process. The limit was reached on the seventy-third day, the day he died in his sleep.

Following the time of De Moivre, there was a transition period. Many advances in the field had been made and it was time to pause, reflect, and place all these facts in usable form. Euler was just the man for the job, because this was his specialty. In the next chapter we shall discuss Euler and his contemporaries in their work of organizing this knowledge.

8

Mr. Euler and His Contemporaries

The Prolific Mr. Euler

Leonard Euler (1707–1783, Swiss) was one of the principal figures in the transition period between the brilliant discoveries of the Bernoullis and De Moivre and the later ones of Laplace. During this time the known facts were assembled and put into clear, concise form. Those which were found to be erroneous were omitted. Switzerland was now doubly endowed, first with the Bernoullis and then Euler.

Paul Euler studied under Jacques Bernoulli I, whereas his son Leonard came under the direction of Johannes I at the University of Basel. Leonard became a great friend of Johannes' sons, Daniel and Nicolaus III, who had an influence on his later life. Paul Euler wanted his son to be a minister and was his teacher along these lines for several years. Fortunately for mathematics he also taught Leonard this subject and it held such a fascination for him that Paul readily consented to the change in vocation. Under the inspiration of Johannes Bernoulli I, Leonard received a master of arts when sixteen. Shortly thereafter he transmitted two papers to the Paris Academy which were of such high caliber that he gained wide recognition.

Euler is reported to have "calculated without apparent effort, as men breathe, or as eagles sustain themselves in the wind." His contemporaries called him "analysis incarnate." Some say he could dash off a mathematical paper in the half hour or so between the first and second calls to dinner. He wrote on theology, medicine, and astronomy, as well as mathematics. Although much of his work is in the field of higher mathematics, he also wrote on elementary topics and some say these writings could be read as easily as a detective thriller.

Many symbols which the high school student uses with little thought of their origin, not only in the field of probability, but of mathematics in general, were first used by Euler. These include e for the base of natural logarithms; a, b, c, for the respective sides of triangle ABC; s for the semiperimeter of triangle ABC; i for the imaginary unit $\sqrt{-1}$; and $\neq$ for not equal to.

He was accustomed to working with many interruptions and often composed with one of his thirteen children in his lap and others playing around him. He is reported to have had an excellent disposition and simplicity of manner. When a newcomer to the field, twenty-three years old, sent a solution to him for a particular problem, Euler wrote the boy to go ahead and publish the result. As it happened, Euler himself had just finished a similar solution, but delayed it so the novice could receive all the credit. This lad turned out to be Joseph Lagrange, and we shall meet him later.

Euler, with his usual systematic method, put the subjects of annuities, insurance, and old-age pensions into the form now familiar to students of mathematics of finance. In the field of probability he continued methodically to put the currently discussed problems in shape.

As was noted earlier, this was a period of transition and even though much of Euler's work on the subject was not original, one finds mention of an opinion held by him or a treatise by him on a particular problem in many of the papers published on the subject of probability. This was true whether it was a discussion of the banker's advantage, an ordinary game of cards, mortality, births, lottery, regular annuities, and even what would happen to the insurance if both husband and wife died. In many cases Euler does not calculate the numerical results, but formulas are left so that the reader may either construct his own tables or work from those already composed. Unfortunately much of Euler's work in probability, although of great importance, is too advanced for the beginning student.

Except for about three weeks he was totally blind during the last seventeen years of his life. During that three weeks he had a cataract removed from his left eye and to his great joy and delight was able to see, but due to either carelessness or lack of knowledge of proper treatment, there was an infection and he was again blind. His early religious education seemed to help him face this bleak future. He prepared for it calmly and began practicing on his blackboard, writing larger and larger. His wits and other perceptions seemed to sharpen as his eyes dimmed. He had an unbelievable memory and essentially memorized all leading formulas in mathematics of his day. His pupils and grandchildren wrote as he dictated and his work continued to flow nearly until his death. He would write the formulas on the blackboard so they could be more readily copied.

It is told that two of his pupils were working on the summation of a series of seventeen terms. They disagreed by one unit in the fiftieth digit. Euler mentally performed the calculations and found their mistake.

One afternoon, probably the way he would have wished it, Euler was working on a mathematical problem. In a short time he asked for his grandson and was talking and drinking tea when he suffered a stroke. His pipe dropped from his mouth and with the words "I die" he ceased his calculations.

Simpson: The Ex-Weaver

Thomas Simpson (1710–1761, English) was living during the period when Newton's majestic shadow was still present, but he is probably the most important English mathematician and textbook writer during the period. It was through texts and popular mathematical periodicals that much of the mathematical knowledge of the day was spread.

Simpson's father was a weaver, and in this working class it was presupposed that the children would apprentice and thus learn the family trade. Any formal education he received, other than ordinary reading of English, was self-taught. His father always became quite angry at Thomas for reading all those "useless books." In fact their quarrels became so violent that Thomas ran away from home.

In spite of the many interruptions which Simpson had in trying to make a living, he still had time to write, and his first treatise appeared in 1737. He customarily directed his work to the average student and his approach was clear and direct. Again writers differ, but some say he was an exceptional teacher, others disagree. The conflict seems to be that in his early years he was a very good teacher, but failed rapidly as he became older. In 1743 he was appointed professor of mathematics in the Royal Academy at Woolwich, which he occupied to his death. Many of his students became leading men in their fields, and it is said that he did much for Woolwich in raising its standards.

The subject of probability attracted Simpson's attention. In 1740 he published *The Nature and Laws of Chance* in four volumes. Simpson stated that it was his desire to bring the known facts of the subject down to the level of ordinary capacities. Actually the work was an abridgment of that by De Moivre. The fact that it contained so little really new material shows that De Moivre had delved into the subject far enough that even the high power of Simpson was unable to find anything very original with the mathematical resources then available. Simpson's book contained a study of the doctrine of combinations and permutations, differences in advantage in lotteries, and various problems with the probability of winning in a specified number of times.

In 1742 Simpson published *The Doctrine of Annuities and Reversions* and complimented De Moivre on his work in the preface. In this there were included valuation tables for single and joint lives which were calculated on the London bills of mortality. This represented an early contribution to the development of insurance. In fact it is reported that the Equitable and Amicable Insurance Societies, two large insurance companies, used these tables in the eighteenth century. By this time Simpson's reputation had spread to the American Colonies where he was highly regarded.

Simpson, as did Newton and many other prominent mathematicians of the period, made numerous contributions to *The Ladies' Diary*, which was a popular magazine published from

1704 until about 1816. Just as present day magazines often publish chess or bridge problems, or crossword puzzles, this magazine often published mathematical problems, ranging from those of an elementary nature to those which were quite advanced. Problems and solutions were presented often under assumed or fictitious names. Problems were sometimes proposed in verse, and often bad verse, but they do show the development of mathematics throughout this period and in particular they show the growing attention which was being paid to probability.

It had formerly been customary to publish results without methods shown, but Simpson tried to make everything as lucid to the general public as possible. It is felt by many that he contributed more to the development of the popular interest in probability than any other, since his results were directed toward the inexperienced reader.

D'Alembert: "I Doubt It"

The contributors to the theory of probability appeared from many walks of life. *Jean-le-Rond D'Alembert* (1717–1783, French) was abandoned by his mother on the steps of the little church in St. Jean-le-Rond. He was found there one cold winter night by a policeman and thus given his Christian name. Apparently he felt D'Alembert added more sophistication because this appeared as an attachment to his name in his later writings. A glazier (one who fits windows with glass) and his wife took the poor orphan, and he repaid them by seeing that they never were in need. They preferred to live in their humble home, where D'Alembert lived with his adopted mother until her death.

He showed an interest in mathematics very early and his foster parents implored him not to waste his time on such useless things.

His natural father apparently continued to support him, and he was left an inheritance by which he could continue his schooling. First he prepared for the bar, later took up medicine, but finally his interest in mathematics and physics was so great that he devoted his life to their study. It is said that his style was brilliant but not polished, which revealed his character—bold, honest, and frank.

During most of the last years of his life he cooperated with the philosopher Diderot in editing the French encyclopedia. The most important of his many articles were on probability and geometry. Just as in the classroom erroneous ideas are cleared up by questions, so in the study of a new subject wrong conclusions reached by men making incorrect inferences are corrected by the attention which is then paid to the specific idea. D'Alembert was thus partly responsible for putting the theory of probability on a sound basis by his opposition to some of the opinions generally accepted. Because he had by this time gained such a high reputation, his ideas were carefully reviewed. One interesting situation arose when probability was applied to medicine. Daniel Bernoulli had been advocating inoculation for smallpox on the basis of the probability of contracting the disease being much smaller among the inoculated persons than among the non-inoculated. D'Alembert did not deny this, but pointed out that there was a probability that a person inoculated would die as a result; if he had not been inoculated he had a high probability of living for several more years.

The controversy fundamentally involves the fact that although more people may be helped than hurt, this is of little comfort to the family of one who dies. It must be remembered that methods of inoculation then used were not as safe as they are today, and there was a real danger involved.

D'Alembert also wrote on the Petersburg problem. He insisted that if the probability of an event were practically zero it should be completely ignored and called zero. His most classic error concerns the following problem: Two players toss a coin which is to be thrown twice. If heads appear on either trial the first player wins, and if a head does not appear at all the second player wins. D'Alembert argues that if the first toss is a head then the first player wins and the game is over, or if the first toss is tails then the first player wins on the second toss if it is heads and the second player wins if it is tails. He therefore erroneously concludes that there are three cases, and the probability of the first player winning should be 2/3. This same type of error is made by the modern student of probability. Two of the correct ways of solving the problem are as follows: First consider the total ways that a coin may fall, denoting T for tails and H for heads. These possibilities are HH, TT, HT, TH. Three ways are favorable to the first player and there are four possible ways the coin may fall, so the probability of the first player winning is 3/4. As a second correct way of attacking the problem, let it be noted that the events "first player wins by getting a head on the first trial" and "first player wins by getting a head on the second trial" are mutually exclusive events. The player wins if *either* one *or* the other of these mutually exclusive events occurs, and the probability of winning on the first *or* the second trial is the sum of the probabilities of winning on the respective trials. The probability of throwing a head on the first trial is 1/2 and the probability of a head on the second trial is (1/2)(1/2), since for the second trial we are here stating that he has obtained a tail on the first trial. His total probability is then (1/2) + (1/2)(1/2) or 3/4 as before.

Condorcet: The Marquis

The subject of probability now travels to a marquis, *Marie Jean Antoine Nicolas Caritat, Marquis de Condorcet* (1743–1794, French). Condorcet was educated at a Jesuit school. His family desired him to be a captain of the cavalry, but he was more interested in writing. His writings were on probability, calculus, and several eulogies to deceased academicians, some of which are still read as classics in French literature.

After Jacob Bernoulli's *Ars Conjectandi* was published there was a brief time in which it was forgotten until Condorcet helped revive interest in it. His best writings were on the subject of probability; however, in many cases he seemed to have made it unnecessarily difficult and in places his notation is poor. For this reason they are now rarely read. Some of his writings were on paradoxes, such as, the reason we feel the sun will rise tomorrow is because it did yesterday, the day before, and so on. Each morning it rises the probability is increased that it will rise the next day. Condorcet applied his principle to a human life, saying that because a person saw the dawn this morning and yesterday morning and as far back as he can remember, then each additional morning they see the dawn the probability will be increased that they will live to see another one. In other words the human life should be infinite. The fallacy here lies in what we call *statistical* or *empirical* probability. Former experience has told us that a person will not live forever, whereas former experience also tells us that the sun will continue to "rise" since it always has as far back as there are historical records. This is contrasted with *mathematical* or a priori probability wherein we know the exact possibilities available. If we throw a die there are only six different ways in which this may fall. Even though we know this from experience, a person who has never thrown a die could observe that fact from the faces. In some treatises Condorcet fails to distinguish between the two types of probability.

Probability was even applied to law. It is noted that men were debating the pros and cons of corporal punishment. Condorcet wrote against it saying that even though the probability is very small that an innocent person would be put to death, the only way of making the probability zero was to ban such a sentence.

Probability was applicable to government. Several works concern voting. Condorcet asserts that the voter must be an intelligent and informed man if the system is to work as it is intended. In one problem he considered three candidates, A, B, and C. Out of sixty votes A receives 23, B obtains 19, and C gets 18. Therefore A is elected. He argues that this is not necessarily good for perhaps the nineteen that voted for B would have preferred C to A. Some of this is now corrected by the 2/3 majority clause.

He and his friends, Laplace and Lagrange, were caught up in the Reign of Terror during the French Revolution. Laplace and Lagrange were able to adequately hide their identity but unfortunately Condorcet gave himself away when he ordered a twelve-egg omelet, obviously a dish for an aristocrat. He was arrested and imprisoned. After his death he was found in his cell with an empty poison ring near him. Many feel he would have been one of our foremost mathematicians if he had not become implicated in the Revolution.

Lambert: The Boastful One

Some authorities classify *Johann Henrich Lambert* (1728–1777, German) as a minor writer. If this is true we then see that major and minor mathematicians of this time as well as those from almost every status were writing on probability. Lambert, like his father, was a tailor. Through his own efforts he learned elementary mathematics. Later he became a tutor and traveled extensively. In his leisure time he was able to turn out many works on astronomy, logarithms, slide rule, psychology, and ballistics, to name just a few.

His humble beginnings were not reflected in his attitude. It is said that when he was interviewed by Frederick the Great he was asked in which science he was most proficient and replied, "All." Then when questioned as to how he attained his mastery of these subjects he answered, "Like the celebrated Pascal, by my own self." This did not endear him to the king.

The Almanacs were enjoying enthusiasm at this time and many people had great faith in them regarding weather and other events. Lambert worked on the possibilities that if this information were thrown out at random, what would be the probability that the predictions would be true. He then was led to a problem which is actually the game of *Treize*, although he does not call it so. This is basically the same problem in which it was asked the probability that at a hat check stand the various hats would be returned to their owners. Lembert deals with letters in envelopes and supposed there to be n letters to be written and n corresponding envelopes. The letters are put at random in the envelopes, and he wants to find the probability that all, or any particular number of letters are in the wrong envelope.

There are $n!$ ways in which the letters can be put into the envelopes and only one way in which all are in the correct place. There is *no* way in which just one letter can be misplaced. If one letter were misplaced, at least one other envelope would contain the wrong letter. The analysis of this problem becomes somewhat involved. Details are available in several standard texts on probability. A very interesting fact which arises from such analysis is that for any value of n greater than four, the value of the probability of at least one correct match remains very nearly the same. To state it another way, if we seek the probability of at least one letter being in its proper envelope, this probability is very nearly the same for ten letters as for a thousand letters. Here is one instance where the number e comes into the picture. It may be proved that as the number of letters increases indefinitely, the probability that exactly no letters are in their correct envelope becomes very nearly $1/e$.

In this chapter we have discussed several mathematicians from the well-known to the lesser-known and from the destitute to those of royal birth. This should give an indication of the vast interest the theory of probability was getting during this period. It might also be noted that the mathematical constant e for the base of our natural logarithms and π are appearing in many unsuspected places in the theory. In the next chapter we shall find an interesting way in which the constant π turns up again in probability.

9

Buffon and Bayes

Buffon: Nature and Needles

In this chapter we find the theory of probability appearing in even more surprising places. *Georges Louis Leclerc Buffon* (1707–1788, French) was a naturalist by occupation. He was educated in a Jesuit college and later appointed keeper of the Royal Gardens and the Museum in Paris. It was at this period of his life that he began his monumental work on natural history, for which he is no doubt best known. Natural history is the science dealing with all objects in nature. The entire work contained forty-four volumes, and he devoted some thirty-nine years of his life to it. This seems to have been the first work on natural history which was compiled in an interesting and intelligible way so that the public at large enjoyed it. Some of the information it contains was later developed by Charles Darwin in his theory of evolution.

In Buffon's work on probability he condemns gambling even when it is done under conditions which are fair. For example he takes up the problem of two people whose wealth is equal and in a particular game each one stakes half of his fortune. The winner will increase his assets by 1/3, whereas the loser will decrease his by 1/2. Buffon concludes that there is more to fear from loss than to hope from gain.

Buffon liked to use the experimental approach. He tossed a coin 4040 times and found that there were 2048 heads. This gave a probability for heads of .507. Practically no one would have expected him to obtain exactly 2020 heads, even though the theoretical probability of a head is 1/2. It seems many people would agree that in the long run one would expect to get approximately the same number of heads, but these same people are surprised to find that this probability, as well as the probability in many other fields, may be actually predicted and computed. It may again be helpful to distinguish between theoretical probability and empirical or experimental probability. In coin tossing if we assume heads and tails are equally likely, then the theoretical probability of a head is 1/2. The empirical probability based on Buffon's experiment is 2048/4040.

We also warn against two false assumptions: It is not true that the more tosses, the more closely does the number of heads approach the number of tails. In Buffon's experiment, the number of heads differs from the number of tails by 56. It would clearly be impossible for this large a discrepancy to occur in 50 tosses, and most unusual in 100 tosses. Recognizing this, some persons feel that as the number of tosses increases, the ratio of heads to tails gets closer and closer to one. The fallacy is seen by an example. If in a given situation there have been 98 tails and 102 heads, the ratio of heads to tails is 102/98. If the next toss is heads the ratio is getting farther away from one, not closer to one.

If one had no additional information it might be expected that the probability of a male birth would be 1/2 and the probability of a female birth also 1/2. However, in the long run one finds that more boys are born than girls. In fact during the years 1939 through 1959 the United States had 1049 boys born to every 1000 girls. Based on this fact we would say the empirical probability of a boy being born is .512 and not .500. Not long ago there was a headline in a newspaper stating that triplets which were born prematurely beat the odds 1500 to 1. This is based on the fact that on the average only one set of triplets out of each 1500 born prematurely survive. Other things such as mortality due to any disease, undertaking of a particular business, and fire and marine insurance are computed on the basis of what has happened in the past.

The problem which has made Buffon's name famous in the history of probability is Buffon's Needle Problem. It was originally performed with a needle, but some matches and a floor with parallel boards will work just as well. The actual formula used can be proved by the methods of the calculus

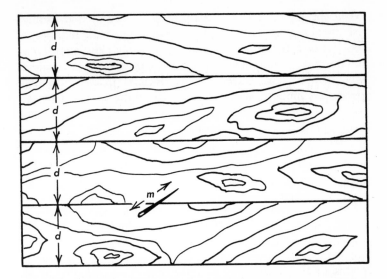

Fig. 9-1. Buffon's needle problem. In the diagram, d is the width of the boards, m is the length of the needle (or match), and p is the probability that the needle will fall across a crack between the boards. It may be found that $\pi = 2m/pd$. Remember that m must be shorter than d.

but the beginner can verify it experimentally very easily. Take any number of matches and toss them on the floor, being certain that the length of the match is *shorter* than the distance between the joints of the parallel boards (see Fig. 9-1). Now count the number of matches which fall on a joint between the boards, disregarding those at the end of a board. Let p represent the probability that a match falls across a joint, m the length of the match, and d the distance between the boards. By the calculus it may be proved that

$$p = 2m/\pi d \quad \text{or} \quad \pi = 2m/dp$$

To avoid matches falling on top of each other, toss one match at a time and remove it after recording the result. Count the number of times a match falls on a joint; divide this by the total number of tosses to obtain your experimental value of p. Measure the length m of the match and the distance d between the joints and then compute π by the second formula just mentioned. Even with a relatively small number of matches or a few tosses, it is surprising how close an approximation may be obtained. One experimenter in 1901 is said to have computed π correct to six decimal places with 3408 tosses, but modern authors are a little dubious about so precise an answer as this. If one has never heard of the method it may sound a little fantastic—so why not try it out for yourself?

Bayes: A Preacher's Probability

Even in the ministry the theory of probability was being studied and expanded. *Reverend Thomas Bayes* (c. 1702–1761, English) devoted much time to the subject, and it is to him that we owe the concept of inverse probability. This concept relates to the probability of unknown causes which are deduced from observed events. Laplace developed the idea further, but it was not put on a sound basis until the 1930's. Bayes was the first to test it inductively, meaning that one reasons from the particular to the general or from a sample to the whole population. The calculus is required in order to effect a complete proof, but some examples will be given which illustrate its use. The general formula may be written as follows:

$$(B_i,A) = \frac{(B_i)(A,B_i)}{(B_1)(A,B_1) + (B_2)(A,B_2) + \ldots + (B_n)(A,B_n)}$$

In this formula $i = 1, 2, 3, \ldots n$, (B_i,A) is the probability that the event B_i will occur when it is assumed that A has already occurred, and (A,B_i) is the probability that the event A will occur when it is assumed that B_i has occurred. In some cases it is known that B has occurred, but for consistency we shall use the wording "A, assuming B has occurred." For example, suppose one has a box containing apples and bananas of different sizes. Let A represent the drawing of an apple and B_i the drawing of a banana of a particular size. A person is blindfolded and draws out the first fruit that he touches. If the drawing of an apple has already assumed to have occurred then (B_i,A) would represent the probability that the next draw would be a banana. If the drawing of a banana were assumed to have occurred (A,B_i) would represent the probability that the next draw would be an apple.

Bayes' formula may be used in various types of inspection processes. Suppose a car manufacturer knows that one car in a thousand has been found to have a certain rather serious defect in the fuel pump. An inspection process is developed which will locate 90 percent of the cars having this defect; however, 10 percent of the cars having the defect will pass inspection. It further develops that of the cars which actually do not have this fuel pump defect, one car in 100 is shown by the inspection process as defective. Let us assume that of a large number of cars produced, a single car is selected at random, given the inspection, and the inspector reports the car has a defective fuel pump. What is the probability that the fuel pump is actually defective? Again Bayes' formula may be applied to find:

$$(B_1,A) = \frac{(B_1)(A,B_1)}{(B_1)(A,B_1) + (B_2)(A,B_2)}$$

$$= \frac{(0.001)(0.9)}{(0.001)(0.9) + (0.999)(0.01)} = 0.083;$$

where (B_1) represents the probability that a car picked at random will have the defect, that is, one in a thousand or 0.001; (B_2) represents the probability that it will not have the defect or 999 out of 1000 or 0.999; (A,B_1) represents the probability of locating the cars with defective fuel pumps or 9 out of 10; and finally (B_1,A) is the probability that the cars included in the inspection process actually do have a defect. It may be noted that although the inspection process seems quite an accurate one, locating 90 per cent of the cars having defective fuel pumps, in its actual operation roughly 8 per cent of the cars caught by this process actually do have a defective fuel pump. Certainly careful consideration must be given to this fact.

In dealing with Bayes' Theorem one nearly always encounters an urn problem. The word *urn* is rarely used any more,

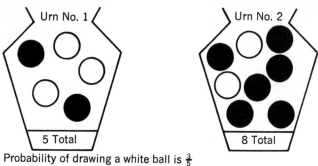

Probability of drawing a white ball is $\frac{3}{5}$
Probability of drawing a black ball is $\frac{2}{5}$

If the transferred ball is black:

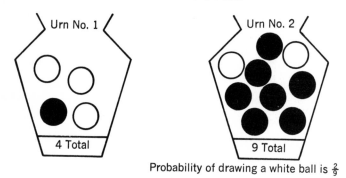

Probability of drawing a white ball is $\frac{2}{9}$

If the transferred ball is white:

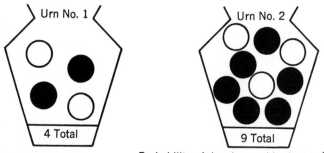

Probability of drawing a white ball is $\frac{3}{9}$

Fig. 9-2.   The urn problem.

but it appears in the literature. We could just as well use the words *box* or *vase*. Suppose two urns contain respectively three white and two black balls, and two white and six black balls. One ball is transferred from the first urn to the second and then a ball is drawn from the second urn. If this ball is white, what is the probability that the transferred ball was black? We have two hypotheses: B_1 that the transferred ball was black and B_2 that it was white, whose probabilities are (see Fig. 9-2):

$$(B_1) = 2/5 \text{ and } (B_2) = 3/5.$$

The probabilities of then drawing a white ball from the second urn are:

$$(A,B_1) = 2/9, (A,B_2) = 3/9.$$

Therefore the probability that the transferred ball was black is given as follows:

$$(B_1,A) = \frac{(2/5)(2/9)}{(2/5)(2/9) + (3/5)(3/9)} = 4/13.$$

Two classic problems will now be discussed. The first is the "Life on Mars" Paradox. This was formulated at a time when there had been little scientific research on Mars. One group raised the question as to the probability of life on Mars. Since they said they were totally ignorant on the subject, on the basis of "insufficient reason," it must be admitted that the answer is 1/2. But if they adopted another approach they could say that the probability of no horses on Mars was 1/2, the probability of no cows on Mars was 1/2, and this could be extended to every class of animal or vegetable. Then the probability of no horses, *and* no cows, *and* . . . n things would be $(1/2)^n$. The probability that there *is* life on Mars plus the probability that there is no life must be certainty or one. Therefore, the probability that there was at least one kind of life on Mars is $1 - (1/2)^n$ which is almost one or almost certainty. By the first argument the probability is 1/2, and by the second reasoning the probability turns out to be almost one. We have therefore obtained two answers to the same question, and there must be an error. This illustrates the care with which the subject must be handled in order to avoid obtaining illogical answers.

Bertrand's "Box Paradox" is another classic example. The problem is sometimes stated as follows: There are three identical boxes each having two drawers. The first box contains a gold coin in each drawer, the second a gold coin in one drawer and a silver coin in the other, and the third has a silver coin in each drawer. A box is chosen at random, and one drawer is opened and found to contain a gold coin. What is the probability that the other drawer also contains a gold coin?

One approach may be to reason as follows: Since each of the gold coins is as likely as the other to be chosen, and since there are two gold to one silver left to be chosen, the probability is given as 2/3. Bayes' Theorem may also be used. Let A_{gg} denote the event that the box with two gold coins is chosen, A_{ss} the event that the box with two silver coins is chosen, B_g the probability that the additional coin one picks up is a gold coin, and so forth. By Bayes' Theorem we may write:

$$(B_g, A_{gg}) = \frac{(A_{gg})(B_g)}{(A_{gg})(B_g) + (A_{ss})(B_g) + (A_{gs})(B_g)},$$
$$= \frac{(1/3)(1)}{(1/3)(1) + (1/3)(0) + (1/3)(1/2)} = 2/3.$$

If one were to choose a box at random and were asked the probability that it contained a coin of different metals, this would be 1/3, and is entirely different from the probability after a known coin is drawn.

One is tempted to reason that after a coin is drawn the other coin is either gold or silver and the probability is 1/2, but this is fallacious reasoning and must be treated with caution.

10

Lagrange, Laplace, and Later

Lagrange: The Good Samaritan

During the latter part of the eighteenth century and the first of the nineteenth, much of the work in the field of mathematics through the calculus began to take on the form and style in which it is now used. *Joseph Louis Lagrange* (1736–1813, French) was one of the foremost men living in this period. It has been said that he was Italian by birth, German by adoption and Parisian by choice. Inasmuch as most of his celebrated works were completed during his stay in France, plus the fact that he was mostly of French descent, he is usually classified as French. This nation is justifiably more than happy to claim him.

He was the youngest of eleven children, but the only one to survive beyond infancy. His mother and father were both wealthy in their own right, but his father was a compulsive speculator. When the time came for Lagrange to inherit the family fortune, there was nothing left to inherit. He reasoned, without bitterness, that if he had had money he probably would not have gone into mathematics, so that it was no doubt for the best. He was not an infant prodigy in the field of mathematics and apparently only became interested in it after reading an essay by Halley. From this time there was no holding him as he rapidly climbed the ladder of mathematical learning. We have mentioned the time he sent a unique solution of a problem to Euler. At a very early age, between sixteen and nineteen, he became professor of mathematics at the Royal Artillery School in Turin, Italy. It seems that the majority of his students were older than he, but he had such a pleasant and quiet manner that they soon accepted him without question. Some historians feel that Lagrange was the ghost writer of many of the fine memoirs published during this period. While in Turin he advanced the theory of probability by applying the differential calculus to it.

Several of the problems upon which he worked dealt with measurement; for example the calculation of the true height of an individual or the measurement of a board. In either of these cases there would be some readings that were larger than the true value and some that were smaller. Lagrange discussed the problem of a cases in which no error was made, b cases in which an error equal to $+1$ unit was made, and an additional b cases in which there was an error equal to -1 unit. The problem is to find the probability that an average of n observations will give an exact result. Lagrange shows that if the expression $[a + b(x + x^{-1})]^n$ is expanded in powers of x and the coefficient of the term not containing x is taken and divided by $(a + 2b)^n$, which is the whole number of cases that may occur, the required probability is thus obtained. In this expression if we let $a = 2$, $b = 3$, $n = 1$, by substitution it is seen that the probability, p, is $2/8$ or $1/4$. If we now let $n = 2$ and the same conditions exist for a and b, the probability is found to be $4/64$ or $1/16$. In general, as n increases the probability that the result shall be exact decreases. Perhaps this is a mathematical approach to an explanation of why it is that the more people one asks about an accident or fire, the more varied are the replies.

In annuities he discussed the following problem: A father desired to make certain his children are all cared for until they have reached "majority" in case of his death. Lagrange reasoned that from experimental probability we may determine the cost of providing an annuity of the desired size for child A during the time this child is a minor. Let this cost be A'. Likewise, let the cost of an annuity of the same size for the minority of child B be represented by B'. Let $(AB)'$ represent the cost of providing an annuity of the specified sum to both child A and B while they are minors. Lagrange demonstrates that the cost of an annuity payable as long as *either* child is a minor is $A' + B' - (AB)'$. (See Fig. 10-1.) He extended the reasoning to the case of three children.

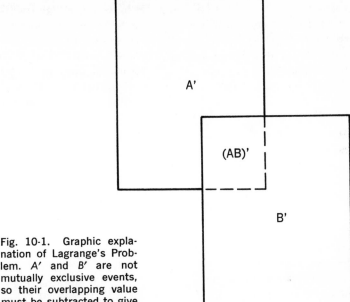

Fig. 10-1. Graphic explanation of Lagrange's Problem. *A'* and *B'* are not mutually exclusive events, so their overlapping value must be subtracted to give the correct sum.

Lagrange was apparently well liked by nearly everyone, and Euler and D'Alembert schemed to get Frederick the Great to request Lagrange's presence in Berlin. It is said that Frederick sent him a message saying that the Greatest King of Europe desires the services of the Greatest Mathematician of Europe. Lagrange was thirty at this time and remained in Berlin for twenty years.

When Frederick died in 1786 Lagrange gladly accepted an invitation from King Louis XVI to work in Paris.

The French Revolution broke out and his friends advised him to leave, but he declined. When his friend, the great French Chemist Lavoisier, lost his head in the guillotine, Lagrange lamented that the execution took only a moment whereas it might take nature one hundred years to produce a likeness of Lavoisier.

One mathematical good which came out of the Revolution was the adoption of the metric system. We may thank Lagrange that this system has ten as its base rather than twelve. After a small amount of calculation most people would agree that it is easier to multiply or divide by ten than by twelve.

Later he was made professor of the newly established École Normale, where he taught until his death in 1813.

Laplace: The Jealous Genius

P. S. Laplace (1749–1827, French) has been given credit for contributing more than any other one person to the theory of probability and has been called the father of the modern phase of it. At the present time there is very little known about his early life. Some feel that this was because he was ashamed of his peasant background. He early displayed an intense interest in mathematics. At the age of eighteen he set off to Paris with several letters of recommendation from the businessmen of his village. When he arrived, he sent these on to D'Alembert, thinking he would be quite impressed and would invite Laplace to visit him. D'Alembert was then enjoying a favorable reputation as an illustrious mathematician. Nothing was heard in reply. Then Laplace sat down and wrote a letter on the principles of mechanics. D'Alembert immediately replied telling him that he paid little attention to recommendations from other people but that Laplace did not need them; his work was recommendation enough.

Nearly all Laplace's accomplishments in astronomy were founded on information which Lagrange had begun, but Laplace did not give anyone else credit unless it was absolutely necessary. He later collaborated with Lagrange on some work. Lagrange never held a grudge and remained on the best terms with Laplace, even though he was not given the credit due him.

At one time Laplace leaned toward the theory of numbers, but realized swiftly that its puzzles would take up more time than he could spare from his work on the solar system. In the work he did with astronomy, it soon became apparent that he needed more information on the theory of probability, and whereas at first he regarded it as a tool for astronomy, he soon saw that it was indispensable to all exact science and devoted his full talents in this direction. In 1812 he published a series of papers which were condensed and collected under the title *Théorie analytique des probabilités.*

In one example Laplace considered the chance one has to throw a given face with a common die in n throws. The chance of not throwing that particular face is $5/6$ in one throw and $(5/6)^n$ in n throws. The chance of throwing this particular face is $1 - (5/6)^n$ if the die is symmetrical. If it is not symmetrical other modifications must be made.

He also poses the problem of births. In twenty-six years it was noticed in Paris that 251,527 boys were born and 241,945 girls. Find the probability that the birth of a boy is greater than $1/2$. This probability was found to differ from unity by less than $1.1521/10^{42}$. In other words it is almost certain to be greater than $1/2$.

Several other problems are developed in connection with the births of boys and girls. He suggested the following problem: Suppose one knows the number of births in a year in a large country such as France, and further suppose that for a certain district both the population and the number of births are known. If one assumes the ratio of the population to the number of births in a year is the same for the whole country as it is for the district, the population for the entire country may be estimated. Laplace investigated the size of the error in such an estimate. After all, in any type of scientific data it is most important to know how certain one can be of a particular answer given and approximately how far off it might be expected to be from the exact value.

Laplace related probability to the mechanics of the sky. In one treatise he stated that out of one hundred comets observed not one had been seen to move in a hyperbola. Laplace proposed to show by the theory of probability that this result would be expected. The probability that a comet would move in an ellipse or parabola is very great, and if it moved in a hyperbola of a great transverse axis it would likely be indistinguishable from a parabola.

Laplace also applied probability to geometry, as evidenced

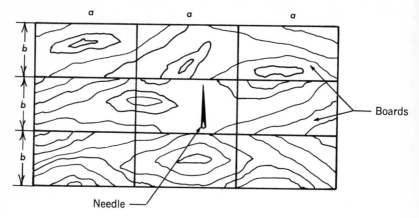

Fig. 10-2.   Laplace's Problem.

by the following problem known as "Laplaces problem" (Fig. 10-2). Suppose a board is broken down into congruent rectangles and a needle is thrown. If the needle is shorter than the smaller side of the rectangle, what is the probability that the needle will lie entirely within one of the rectangles? If we let a equal the length of the longer side and b the shorter side of the rectangle which contains the middle point of the needle of length L, it may be found by the calculus that the required probability is

$$p = 1 - \frac{2L(a + b) - L^2}{\pi \, ab}$$

Buffon's problem is a special case of this one in which the side becomes indefinitely long so that $q = 2L/\pi b$, where q is $1 - p$, that is, that the needle *will* fall on one of the lines.

Another example of probability applied to a geometrical problem is as follows:

On a line, mark off a unit length, AB and pick two points at random on the segment. What is the probability that the three segments of the line thus determined can form a triangle? For simplicity, we chose the line segment, AB, as one unit in length and let the two random points be represented by x and y.

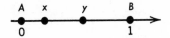

In order to form a triangle, the sum of any two sides must be greater than the third side; giving us the following three inequalities:

$$x + (1 - y) > (y - x) \text{ or } y - x < \tfrac{1}{2}$$
$$(y - x) + (1 - y) > x \text{ or } \quad x < \tfrac{1}{2}$$
$$(y - x) + x > (1 - y) \text{ or } \quad y > \tfrac{1}{2}$$

The points which represent *all three* of these inequalities are represented by the shaded area in the following graph.

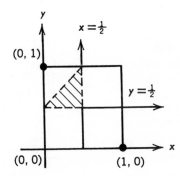

There is a second possible arrangement in which y precedes x.

This arrangement gives three new inequalities as follows:

$$y + (1 - x) > (x - y) \text{ or } x - y < \tfrac{1}{2}$$
$$(x - y) + (1 - x) > y \text{ or } \quad y < \tfrac{1}{2}$$
$$(x - y) + y > (1 - x) \text{ or } \quad x > \tfrac{1}{2}$$

In this case, the points which satisfy *all three* of the inequalities are represented by the following new graph.

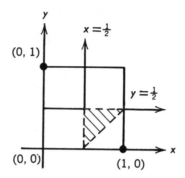

As can readily be seen, the shaded areas representing the required points in each case is 1/8 of the area of the graphs. Thus to satisfy *either* of the cases the probability is the *sum*, or $1/8 + 1/8 = 1/4$.

Laplace's work in probability came in handy for him during the French Revolution. In fact it helped him save his head. He was given the job of working with artillery fire, and computing the chance of over- or under-shooting the target. Napoleon made him a count and later minister of the interior; a position he held for only six months, because of his eccentricities.

Some historians feel that there were four contributions to the theory of probability which overshadowed all the rest. The first was the work of Jacob Bernoulli, the second De Moivre's *Doctrine of Chances*, the third dealt with Bayes' Inverse Probability, and the fourth was the outstanding work by Laplace. In fact it was Laplace himself who gave the classic "definition" of probability—if an event can result in n equally likely outcomes, then the probability of such an event E is the ratio of the number of outcomes favorable to E to the total number of outcomes.

Much of Laplace's work is difficult to read and sometimes vague, but it has been very important to the advancement of probability. Laplace is said to have felt that one of the greatest contributions of probability is to teach us to mistrust our first impressions and only to reach conclusions after research has been made on the subject.

Gauss: The Profound Prodigy

Carl Friedrich Gauss (1777–1855, German) thought very highly of mathematics as a science, and felt that mathematics often condescends to assist astronomy and the other natural sciences, the first place still being mathematics' due.

Many historians feel Gauss is one of the three greatest mathematicians history has produced, Archimedes and Newton being the other two. There has been a voluminous amount of material written about him. In numerous books on mathematics and physics one may find his name in connection with work he has done. He has been called the last universalist, since subsequent to his time the various fields of mathematics have become so involved that it would be practically impossible for any one man to know any appreciable amount about all of them.

It is therefore out of the question to give a full account, or even a very good brief account of his many and varied interests. The outline of his life is limited to a few of the incidents and just a rough sketch of some of his more important accomplishments.

His father was a bricklayer and a gardener, an honest and hard working man, but reportedly a little dumb. When Gauss was about age three his father had been working on some accounts. After he finished adding a column of figures young Gauss told him a mistake had been made and what the correct sum should be. In later years he joked that he could calculate before he could talk.

For his doctoral thesis he submitted the proof of the so-called "Fundamental Theory of Algebra," which states that every polynomial equation of degree one or higher has a root. *Gaussian integers* are numbers of the form $a + bi$ where a and b are integers and $i = \sqrt{-1}$, as plotted in Fig. 10-3.

In appreciation of his exceptional work in physics, there is the electrical unit, a gauss, named for him. His work in electricity and magnetism is unsurpassed, and he also did research in the field of optics.

His interest in probability is scattered throughout many of

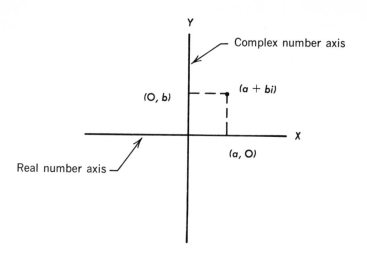

Fig. 10-3. Graph of Gaussian integers or complex numbers.

his treatises. It seems that his earliest interest was from his work in astronomy and geodesy, the latter being that branch of applied mathematics dealing with the shape and area of large portions of the countryside as well as the exact position of geographical points and the curvature, shape and dimensions of the earth. In 1812 a comet appeared which the superstituous people of the day watched with horror and fear. Gauss took delight in seeing it follow the exact path which he had calculated for it.

In connection with readings which he made "on land and in the air" he was struck by the way these sightings would differ, even under the same conditions. This led him on to the theory of errors, and the Method of Least Squares, and finally to the normal or "Gaussian" probability curve. As has been noted, the normal curve was studied by De Moivre, but Gauss was the first who endeavored to justify it by means of the theory of probability.

His powers of concentration were said to be so great that when a servant rushed in to tell him his wife was dying, he replied, "Tell her to wait until I've finished here." In 1807 he was made the director of the new observatory at Göttingen where, except for two or three uneventful trips, he stayed and slept under its roof until his death in his seventy-eighth year.

De Morgan: The Arbitrator

Augustus De Morgan (1806–1871, English) is pictured as an affable, witty, and pleasing man. It has been said that perhaps he would have gained more fame if he had dealt with just one subject, but that he would not have been as interesting. He was one of the persons brought in to mediate the Newton-Leibniz controversy in calculus, and showed his fellow Englishmen that perhaps they had not been entirely fair to Leibniz.

De Morgan's contributions to the theory of probability remain among the foremost in England. He was one of the first to simplify the subject so the layman with no more mathematics than arithmetic could understand it. Whether he succeeded is debatable but at least this was his intention. He expressed a desire for the common man to be able to use probability other than for ordinary games of chance. His work contains some information on its application to life insurance and a few other related topics, but is full of advice to people against drawing unwarranted conclusions without a sound basis for their opinions. He frequently referred to the normal curve and felt everyone would benefit from a thorough study of it.

After his earlier work he wrote an article on the theory of probability in which he discussed more advanced problems.

In the field of law he questions the English practice of requiring a unanimous decision from the jury. He indicated that if a study were made of five hundred trials in which the jury delivered an immediate verdict, it might show a different percentage of error than five hundred trials in which the jury took two hours or more to reach a decision. Questions such as this are discussed today. What is the probability that a unanimous verdict is more correct than one reached by a two-thirds majority vote?

Tchebysheff: Peer to Pauper

Pafnutii Lvovitch Tchebysheff (also Tshebysheff or Cheby-
shev, and other variations in spelling, 1821–1894, Russian) is
considered one of Russia's most celebrated mathematicians.
As a small boy he became intrigued with mechanical inven-
tions, and it is said during his first lesson in geometry he saw
its relationship to mechanics.

His father lost all the family fortune in the famine of 1840,
and thereafter Tchebysheff found it necessary to scrimp and
save for himself and his parents. He never married but devoted his entire life to science and teaching. He cooperated in
collecting two volumes of Euler's work and thereby became
interested in the theory of numbers. In one problem, known
as Tchebysheff's Problem, he related probability to the theory
of numbers and asked: If two positive integers a and b are
chosen at random, what is the probability that a/b is in its
lowest terms. After a rather lengthy computation he finds this
probability to be approximately $2/3$.

Many statistics and probability texts state Tchebysheff's
theorem. By proper use of this theorem one may answer either
of the following questions which are frequently of interest:

1. What is the probability that an item lies not more
   than a specified distance from the average?
2. How wide an interval must we take to be relatively certain that this interval, on either side of
   the average value, will include a specified percentage of the data?

The present chapter discussed concepts which evolved during the last part of the nineteenth century. The following
chapter "Present Patterns" attempts to bring the theory up-to-
date. Unfortunately, much of the work of the present century
which deals with probability involves mathematics of a more
advanced nature than most secondary students have encountered.

11

Present Patterns

Todhunter: The Historian

Isaac Todhunter (1820–1884, English) is considered the Father of the History of Probability and has written the most comprehensive and extensive history of probability to date. Many of his discussions are lengthy, and some even dull, but it remains a very good reference on the subject.

Todhunter was the son of a minister, whose death left the family in a desperate financial condition. His mother opened a school in order to make the living, and Isaac was therefore enabled to continue his learning. He was a shy boy but was always a conscientious worker. He was a pupil of De Morgan who greatly influenced his life and plausibly was the reason for Todhunter's interest in probability. He became a college lecturer and private tutor, but it was his textbook writing that made him financially independent. It is believed that no mathematical treatments on elementary subjects were ever more widely circulated than were Todhunter's. They were even translated into some of the Oriental languages. He also wrote on some more advanced topics, but these did not gain the wide reputation of his elementary books.

Todhunter was a student of foreign literature; his habits and tastes were simple; and he has been described as a kind and gentle man with a warm and sympathetic disposition. He suffered an attack of paralysis which finally brought his studious life to an end.

Venn: The Logician

At this time men of learning were beginning to question the very foundations of probability. Various theories were being

expounded. *John Venn* (1834–1923, English) was one of the
first propounders of approaching the subject from the standpoint of logic, the science which investigates the principles
governing correct or reliable reasoning. There had been a
vague notion of this approach previously, but it was not clear-
cut. Many of his arguments are now discounted, but his book,
The Logic of Chance, is most readable. It is proposed that a
person only knowing arithmetic would understand it, and his
approaches to many of the topics are indeed unique. He suggests that probability should be handled by the philosophers
rather than by the mathematicians. It is feared that he is sometimes correct in stating that once a student connects probability with mathematics, he may be further deterred from
examining it any closer. In one example he points out that
many people feel all cows chew their cuds. He then introduces
probability by showing this view to be based on the fact that
all cows we have seen do, and the more cows we see, the more
we believe this to be a universal trait.

Other topics which he discusses are life expectancy and the
law of error. He warns that in applying probability on the
basis of past events, we must be certain we are dealing with
"like" objects. One may expect to live to be a certain age
because in the past it has been shown on the average that a
person lives to be that age. This is based on the fact that all
people have similarly constructed bodies and cannot be compared with the life expectancy of a horse or a puppy. As an
example of randomness he reminds one that if a sheet of paper
were placed out during the rain we would expect eventually
for it to be completely wet, even though we may not predict
the exact spot on which a particular raindrop will fall.

In the case of lotteries he asks the following: If there are
100 tickets and 10 prizes, would it be fair to assume that a
man may be assured of a prize 1/10 of the time? Even the
mention of lotteries should give a person an idea that this is
not true. This is an example of the subjective side of probability.

If the chance of a person dying in a year is 1/10 and the
chance of his dying of a particular disease is 1/100, then his

chance of dying from something other than this disease is
$1/10 - 1/100$ or $9/100$. To illustrate inverse probability, Venn
presents the problem of the average number of people dying

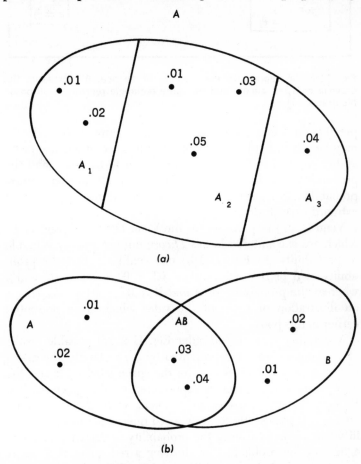

(a)

(b)

Fig. 11-1. (a) the probability of event A is equal to the sum of the
probabilities of A_1, A_2, and A_3 or

$$(.01+.02) + (.01+.03+.05) + (.04) = .16$$

(b) the probability of event A, given the occurrence of event B, is
represented by the overlapping area AB and is

$$\frac{.03 + .04}{.03 + .04 + .02 + .01} = .70$$

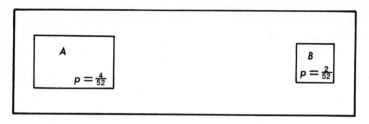

Fig. 11-2. A represents the drawing of an ace, B represents the drawing of a red queen, and the large rectangle represents all possible draws.

per thousand in a particular year. How many of these deaths may be attributed to bronchitis? The problem in inverse probability would be: If a man were known to be dead, find the probability that it was due to bronchitis. He further applies probability to legal testimonies and even to the credibility of extraordinary stories.

Venn is also responsible for the *Venn Diagrams* (Fig. 11-1), which are encountered in *Set Theory* but are equally valuable in probability. In Fig. 11-1(b) one could say that the probability of *A or B* is .02 + .01 + .03 + .04 + .01 + .02 = .13, whereas the probability of *A and B* is .03 + .04 = .07. This is an illustration of some of the rules which were presented earlier in this book.

As another example, consider Fig. 11-2. All possible results of drawing a card are represented by the rectangle; the drawing of an ace is represented by the space labeled *A*; and the drawing of a red queen is represented by the space marked *B*. Note that these spaces are *mutually exclusive*; if we draw an ace it is impossible to draw a red queen. Because there are fifty-two cards in a deck, the probability of drawing an ace is 4/52 and the probability of drawing a red queen is 2/52. If one were asked the probability of *A or B* this may be represented by the *sum* of the probabilities, or in this case 4/52 + 2/52 = 6/52.

Now suppose the events are *not* mutually exclusive. For example, let *A* represent the drawing of a spade whose probability would be 13/52, and let *B* represent the probability of drawing a black face card with probability 6/52. The probability of A or B is not the sum of the probabilities.

The Venn diagram may help (Fig. 11-3). As before, let the rectangle represent all possible drawings; let A represent the drawing of a spade and B the drawing of a black face card. The areas which represent A and B now overlap, since the drawing of a jack, king, or queen of spades satisfies both A and B. Hence, with events which are not mutually exclusive, the probability of A or B is the probability of A plus the probability of B *minus* the probability of the occurrence of an event satisfying both A and B or $13/52 + 6/52 - 3/52 = 4/13$.

Peirce: The Pragmatist

As mentioned before, at this time many of the writers on probability were primarily logicians. Their writings and a few examples will be cited, but no attempt will be made to cover the field of logic. One of the foremost thinkers that the United States has produced was *Charles Sanders Peirce* (1839–1914, American) whose philosophy was later termed "pragmatism," meaning the concept by which nothing is significant except as pertains to its usefulness.

Charles was the second son of Benjamin Peirce who was a Harvard professor and an outstanding mathematician in his time. It seems that Charles' father was quite strict and de-

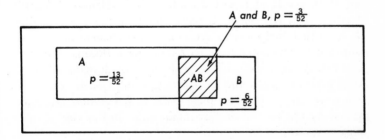

Fig. 11-3. A represents the drawing of a spade, B represents the drawing of a black face card, AB represents the drawing of a spade face card, and the large rectangle represents all possible draws.

manding of him. It is said that they would play a game of concentration from ten in the evening until the following morning and each mistake was rigorously criticized. For a time Charles was a poor student at Harvard, and some say it was in rebellion to the intense demands of his father. However, he subsequently received a degree in chemistry, summa cum laude, an honor which had previously never been attached to any degree in chemistry by Harvard. Much of his later work showed brilliant thinking. Peirce was the first American representative to the International Geodetic Congress and worked for it some thirty years of his life.

Peirce was an incessant worker and many times wrote continuously from one paper to another. In his usual unsystematic way, however, these were not kept in order so many have been unpublished. He wrote all the definitions on some half dozen subjects for the *Century Dictionary*, produced many translations, and even prepared a thesaurus.

In one treatise "The Red and the Black" he says that the theory of probability is simply the science of logic quantatively treated. Either an item is true or false, and these can be replaced by the numbers one and zero respectively, so that each problem in probability is just the general problem of logic. At one place he supposes there are two packs of cards, one containing twenty-five red and one black, and another containing twenty-five black and one red. If a person draws a red card he would have eternal happiness whereas the drawing of a black one would reduce him to everlasting woe. Obviously it would be wise to draw from the pack containing only one black. If, however, he happened to draw the black card, it would be no consolation to him to know that the probability had been in his favor. This reasoning could be extended to the casualties of war, or accidents on the highway or in a storm. It does not help much to tell the victims that the odds were for them. In the long run, says Peirce, all life depends on probability.

According to some he could write a question with one hand and simultaneously complete the solution with the other hand. In spite of his capabilities he never had a permanent teaching position and was usually out of money. He built a vanishing stairway to his attic so he could write in peace without being disturbed by anyone, including his creditors. His last years were completed in poverty and illness, taking a grain of morphine each day to help deaden the pain of cancer. Even though his works were not fully appreciated during his lifetime, he is today called one of the most profound and original of American philosophic thinkers.

Poincaré: Another Last?

It may be recalled that Gauss was called the Last Universalist. However, *Jules Henri Poincaré* (1854–1912, French) was another universalist. Mathematics is sometimes considered to be divided into four parts: arithmetic, algebra, geometry, and analysis. Some would add a fifth division: statistics. It is believed impossible for any one man today to be proficient in more than two of these fields. When he was five Poincaré had diphtheria and for nine months his larynx was paralyzed. This misfortune left him shy and delicate. Throughout his entire life he continued to have poor physical coordination, and his thoughts came so much faster than his tongue could work that it was difficult to understand him. His eyesight was poor, so he cultivated the habit of learning by ear and usually did not take notes in class. His memory was exceptional and once he read a book or learned a fact it remained his to command.

In 1886 Poincaré was promoted to professor of mathematical physics and the calculus of probabilities. He was author of one treatise, "Chance," in which he discussed all the different meanings of chance. He felt that many times we attribute the unknown causes behind an event to chance just because we do not know these causes. For example meteorologists many times have trouble predicting the weather so some people think it is all due to chance, but there are many, many factors acting on the conditions present. Poincaré felt that if one could measure all these other factors it could be seen that chance was not the cause. Suppose a person shuffles a deck of cards many times, or a chemist mixes liquids and powders an extremely large number of times. Each time there could be a different permutation of the cards or of the ingredients and finally all possible arrangements would become equally probable. In this case chance does enter in. If one had 10,000 cards numbered 1 to ·10,000, each number would have the same probability of 1/10,000 of being drawn. He stated that a person might be surprised to draw the number 10,000 whereas it has just as much chance of being drawn as any other number.

Many of our scientific experiments would be impossible if we did not rely on chance or probability. It follows that if an event happens more times than would occur from pure chance alone, we declare that there is a law involved, that is, something other than chance is operating to produce the event.

During his life Poincaré completed about five hundred papers on *new* mathematics. He also discussed questions raised by others. Some feel that if he had been as strong in the practical sciences as in the theoretical we could have rightfully given him the title of the fourth great mathematician. Poincaré was ill during the last four years of his life and died at the height of his powers.

Markoff and His Chains

A. A. Markoff (or Markov, 1856–1922, Russian) was a student of Tchebysheff and displayed brilliance in his work on the theory of probability and mathematical statistics. His chain theory has been developed by prominent mathematicians and recently has gained popularity for its use to the social and biological sciences. Entire books and courses in colleges and universities are devoted to the study of these chains. Basically the chain may be visualized as a process which moves from place to place. The probability at any given stage then determines or at least suggests the probability for the next stage.

An application of these chains could be made in predicting the weather. If the average weather for a particular place were known, and it was further known to be raining on a particular day, it is possible to predict how many additional nice days there will be before another rainy day. Markoff chains are applied to "Random Walks," which are a succession of "walks" along a particular path. The direction of each "walk" or path is determined in a random way. Suppose a blind man by mistake walks out on the roof of a building. If in his walk he encounters a brick chimney, he turns 90° to his right; if he encounters a metal pipe he turns 90° to his left; if he meets a solid wall, he reverses his direction. His action at any turn depends upon what previously happened. If the roof has walls on three sides but is open at the fourth, what is the probability that the blind man does not fall off the roof? We may add the information about the number of chimneys and pipes. This is basically what is done in the kinetic theory of gases where each molecule has the same probability of going to the left as to the right. Of course there are many other variables which must be considered.

In the following tree diagram (Fig. 11-4), which is a Markoff chain, we see the probability of various possible sequences of events in the performance of student John Doe.

Student John Doe is certainly inconsistent. He never writes two perfect test papers in succession. If he does write a perfect paper, he has an even chance of failing the next test, or of being absent. If he fails or is absent there is an even chance that his record will be the same for the next test; if his record changes from absence or failure, 50 percent of the time the change will be to a perfect paper. This information is illustrated in the Tree Diagram. Let E be the event of a perfect paper, A an absence, and F a failure. John Doe's activities then occur with the probabilities shown in Fig. 11–4.

The Markoff chains find further application in sports. In the World Series the probability is computed at the beginning and at any given stage of the Series that one or the other of the teams shall win. In genetics one takes the possible combinations of parents and the probability of inherited characteristics and then finds the probability of the various features of the offspring. A Markoff or enchained probability is then one which is concerned with successive probabilities in which the value of the probability of a variable at a given time and

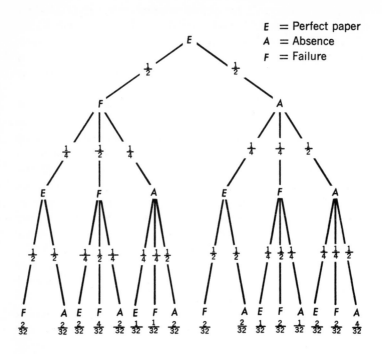

Fig. 11-4. A tree diagram of a Markoff chain showing the probability of various sequences of events in the performance of student John Doe.

place depends on the values obtained from the preceding variables.

Many times in treating these subjects the masses of data are tremendous, and it is here that high-speed computers are invaluable. Many studies would be impossible without them because by the time the analysis of the data became available, the conditions would have changed or the problem might no longer be a current one.

Markoff made many contributions to statistics and advanced much of Tchebysheff's work. He is credited with helping to complete the theory of sampling within the framework of the theory of probability. Apparently very little has been written about his personal life, but from past events the probability of more of these facts being made available increases with the time elapsing since his death.

Keynes: The Economist

John Maynard Keynes, first Baron of Tilton (1883–1946, English) was not satisfied to let his talents rest solely on one of his favorite subjects, mathematics, but sought to apply its rules to society. He apparently had the capacity for looking at a problem, seeing the answer, and then by his forceful personality, advancing his own ideas. His influence has been felt on the economic policy of many democratic nations.

Keynes was born at Cambridge into a family who valued intellectual thoughts. His father was a logician and political economist and his mother, at age ninety-two, wrote *Gathering up the Threads*, depicting various incidents of the family.

The subject of gambling intrigued Keynes. Not only was he an outright gambler, but he also applied his talents to the stock market. He wrote *Treaties on Probability* in which he essentially states the following: Part of our knowledge we obtain directly and the other part by argument, the theory of probability dealing with the latter. The terms *certain* and *probable* exhibit various degrees of belief. In other words probability is just a certain level of the degree of certainty. Even ordinary circumstances of life have a probability. For example if we go for a walk there is a probability that we will arrive home safely.

In 1937 he became seriously ill of a heart ailment and his physician advised him to slow his speed which he did for only a short period of time. He was willing to make any sacrifice his country wished or needed. As head of the British delegation to the United Nations Monetary and Financial conference at Bretton Woods, New Hampshire, he pursued the ideas of a world bank and stabilization of international currency. He was also engaged in negotiating terms of "lend-lease" with the United States. In 1946 he returned from Bretton Woods on the verge of collapse and died of a heart attack in a few days.

Mises: An American Gain

In the same year in which Keynes was born, *Richard von Mises* (1883–1953, American) was born in Austria. He received his education in Vienna. During World War I he served as organizer, teacher, and pilot in the Austrian Air Force. He later became a lecturer in Harvard and was naturalized as a citizen of the United States in 1946. His writings are in many fields of physics as well as in probability and statistics.

The title of one of his books, *Probability, Statistics, and Truth,* came from the remark made by someone that there are three kinds of lies: defensive lies, which are justifiable; base lies, which have no justification; and statistics. He agrees that much nonsense is presented to the public as statistics, but proposes to show that if one starts from statistical observations it is possible to reach conclusions which are just as reliable as those obtained by any other scientific method.

He presents the famous "Problem of Points" proposed to Pascal by Chevalier de Méré concerning the division of stakes if one person wants to leave the game before it is finished. You will recall that probability is sometimes said to have begun with this problem. Subjects which may be treated by statistics are discussed, such as birth and death rates, marriages, suicides, incomes, heredity, and mass production. In these fields one usually draws general conclusions from previous results and predicts future similar happenings. In his treatment of games he states there must be a distinction made between games of chance and games of skill. Chess is a game of skill, whereas any fair card game is a game of chance, if only by the randomness in which the cards are distributed.

Mises was a prolific writer and contributed more than one hundred papers to the scientific world.

Wiener: Ex-Prodigy

Norbert Wiener (1894–   , American) has written several books, among which are *Ex-Prodigy* and *I Am a Mathematician.* These books are excellently written and are inspiring and informative to anyone reading them.

Wiener was born in Columbia, Missouri where his father taught languages at the University of Missouri. The family later moved and he was educated at Tufts College and at Cornell, Harvard, Cambridge, Göttingen, and Columbia Universities. In 1919 he joined the faculty at Massachusetts Institute of Technology and has been there since. He entered college before he was twelve, obtained a bachelor's degree before he was fifteen and the doctorate before he was nineteen. One chapter of the book about his childhood is entitled "College Man in Short Trousers" which almost tells the story itself.

Wiener has been called one of the top six United States mathematicians today. He has written on numerous subjects such as fields of relativity and probability theory. He is founder of the science of cybernetics which has been called a theory dealing with the relationships between control mechanisms in human beings and in machines. Wiener feels that probability is the tying link between physics and mathematics.

Upon coming to Massachusetts Institute of Technology, he desired a problem which would be the center of his work. It was suggested that much was being done with generalizing the concept of probability to cover occurrences being studied not by points or dots but more like a path in space. For example, a one-point problem might deal with the distribution of bullet holes in a target. It could be told in advance the probability that they would tend to cluster about the bull's-eye. A path probability problem would be to characterize the flight of a bee or the rambling of a drunken man. If the man were put in the center of a square how long would it take him to get out of the square? This is essentially the problem of the blind man walking on the roof which was discussed earlier.

At this stage in our study of probability it is almost impossible to keep it separate from the study of statistics which was actually an outgrowth of it. The following chapter will attempt to clarify the relationship between probability and statistics.

12

A Child of Probability

From the preceding material it is seen that the history of probability and the history of statistics are very much entwined. In the study of statistics we are interested in summarizing, classifying, and tabulating huge masses of data which would have little or no meaning otherwise. We saw earlier that John Graunt is said to have founded statistics, and various other men who we have mentioned worked in the field to some extent. In this chapter we shall include other names which will help complete the entire picture.

Poisson: The Human Pendulum

Siméon Denis Poisson (1781–1840, French) used to tell the story of his father finding him one day, where his nurse had left him, suspended from a thin cord attached to a nail in the wall. The small animals and bugs which roamed around the floor would therefore not bother him. He was able to swing himself back and forth, so very early in life gained some firsthand experience with the pendulum, the study of which later occupied much of his time.

In school he attracted the attention of Lagrange and Laplace. A leading analyst in his time, he wrote on probability, mathematical physics, and pure mathematics. His family had greatly hoped that he would become a physician, and when this failed they tried various other occupations for him, but to no avail. Finally they encouraged him to be a lawyer. Fortunately he became interested in mathematics and his contributions to this field are many and great.

Many phases of probability and statistics, such as the Poisson frequency distribution and the Poisson cumulative distribution function are associated with his name. There are many distributions which fit the normal distribution curve; however, it has been noted that some distributions are of another form. A classic problem, resulting in a distribution not of the normal type, is the number of soldiers in a Prussian Army Corps who died each year from the kick of a horse. The number of soldiers involved who might so die is large, but the probability of any one soldier so dying is very small. A more modern application concerns the number of atoms in a radioactive sample which will disintegrate in a unit of time; another might involve the likelihood of a busy signal on the telephone arising from a malfunction of the equipment. For such problems use is often made of a distribution credited to Poisson giving a mathematical model which, to a reasonable degree, approximates the actual situation, and may be of value in the analysis of rare events. In other words, if in some analysis the probability of the event decreases as the number of cases increases, the distribution is of the Poisson type. The mathematics involved in the derivation of the formula for such a distribution is beyond the scope of this book but is available in standard texts.

Quetelet: The Father of Modern Statistics

Lambert Adolphe Jacques Quetelet (1796–1874, Belgian) was teaching mathematics at the age of seventeen in a private school. He studied the subject of probability under Laplace and was no doubt thus enticed to do further work in probability and its related subject, statistics. However, this enthusiasm more than made up for the sometimes erroneous conjectures which he made in statistics. It was due to his suggestion that the London Statistical Society was formed in 1834, and under his incentive the first International Statistical Congress met in Brussels in 1853. It was one of his desires to see international cooperation in statistical matters, and he continued to write on various topics in statistics. He analyzed the first Belgian census, which was the first statistical breakdown of a national census.

In noting the constancy of crimes he bemoaned the fact that one could approximately predict the number of individuals who would stain their hands in the blood of their fellow man, the number of forgers, poisoners, and so on, but yet we have to pay for this "frightful regularity" in prisons. He applied the theory of probability to "the average man." He asserted that statistics had invaded the heavens and that moral and intellectual qualities were measurable. To the people of the day this was too much so they scoffed at him. It remained for World Wars I and II to show mankind that intelligence testing was not immoral. In theory, by the use of tests of intellectual ability, one might determine occupations for which soldiers are fitted, or perhaps unfitted. One such story tells of a lieutenant in charge of testing who reported that a certain soldier should be discharged, because his mental ability was so low that he was utterly unfitted to perform any military duties. The top sergeant observed: "Whatever your fool tests may show, that man is the best mule driver the army ever saw." At any rate it is said that the United States army accomplished in a few months what Quetelet and his followers were unable to do in seventy years. The earliest educational statistics in the United States were carried on by advocates of Quetelet's methods.

Bravais: A Pioneer

Auguste Bravais (1811–1863, French) seems to have begun the work in correlation. Correlation means the co-relationship between paired sets of items. For example, for any student we could have paired items of his weight in pounds and his height in inches. Correlation attempts to answer the question: Do tall students tend to weigh more than the average? Another example of a paired sets of items would be the heights of a father and the height of his first son. Does a short father tend to have a short son and a tall father a tall son? Is there a relationship between the number of miles a tire has been driven and the thickness of the tread remaining? Here the paired items are miles driven and tread thickness. We find that in general tall fathers tend to have tall sons; in other words the more the inches in the father's height, the more inches in the son's height. But in the case of tires, the more miles driven, the less the tread thickness. In the first case we have what is called direct or positive correlation. In the second case we have inverse or negative correlation. There has been found a good correlation between grades a student makes in high school and his probable chance of success in college. In fact this is one of the most widely used criteria for this information.

There have recently been studies showing that the more a high school student is allowed to drive a car, the lower his grades. If this is true we have an example of negative correlation. Medical schools have conducted studies showing the relationship between the longer arm bone and the height of an individual. Some of these studies have proved useful in helping to identify victims in a disaster—often in a negative way, showing that certain bones could not within reasonable probability have belonged to a certain person.

Any number of items may be correlated. There have been studies made which show a high correlation between the size shoe a person wears and his intelligence; between yearly consumption of alcoholic liquors and total salary paid public schoolteachers; between birth rates and number of stork nests in certain European cities. These and other examples demonstrate that blind use of statistics may produce absurd results.

Some of the methods used by Bravais in his correlation theory were not as refined as those we now use but the basic principles were the same.

Galton: The Master Measurer

Francis Galton (1822–1911, English) is said not to have been a mathematician but was mathematically minded. His insatiable quest for facts led him to the measurement of legs, arms, noses, and other traits. He was one of the first to believe that a person's fingerprints do not change through his life and made one of the first systematic studies of this subject. He compiled statistics on travel, mountain climbing, laws of heredity, history of twins, frequency of yawns, number of "twitches" per minute among people listening to lectures, and anything else that was capable of measurement. As founder of the School of Eugenics in England he was led to the study of correlation and other related statistical computations. Eugenics is the science of improving the human race by selection of parents having the most desirable traits.

It is reported that Galton could read before the age of three and wrote a letter before he was four. In fact in the study of gifted children the life of Galton is usually taken up in some detail. He was a cousin of Charles Darwin. His parents wanted him to become a physician, so he went through the motions but was rather unenthusiastic about it all. Upon the death of his father he was left with enough money to travel extensively. His trips led him to the Danube River, Egypt, and into many heretofore unexplored parts of Africa. It was on these ventures that he studied and recorded much data which resulted in some of his works on measurement. Karl Pearson devoted four entire volumes to a biography of Galton's life which was filled with many adventures and an abundant amount of scientific work.

The regression phenomenon was first observed by Galton in relation to heights of individuals. He noted that there is an average which tends to be met. In other words if a father is above average in height his sons will also tend to be above average in height. However, it is also true that in general the height of the sons will not exceed the average as much as the height of the father. Likewise, short fathers tend to have short sons; but again the height of the son is unlikely to be below the average as much as the height of the father. The heights seem to "regress" toward the average. Galton gave the name "regression" to this concept. In present usage it has come to mean much more than this.

Sometimes Galton did not take into consideration all the facts, but his basic principles were well founded. His Law of Heredity states that a person's father and mother each have an influence of one-half upon the child's characteristics, the probability of each being equal. Likewise one-fourth of a person's characteristics can be accredited to each of the four grandparents, and one-eighth each to the eight great-grandparents. Subsequent studies show that this is entirely too elementary a concept, but it was a step in the right direction. His study of the survival of family names is apparently the first chain reaction studied by the methods of probability.

The measure commonly called an average is obtained by adding the various items and dividing by the number of items. For many purposes this is a very satisfactory measure, but there are cases where this is not true. If in a small group of high school students, perhaps twenty-five, each person wrote down the amount of money they spent the previous week, the amounts might be added and divided by twenty-five, giving the arithmetic average. But if one was the son of very wealthy parents, and he purchased a convertible last week, this average would certainly be far from representative of the group. For a situation such as this Galton proposed the *median*, which could be thought of as simply the middle item; in other words half the group spent more than this amount and half spent less. For some purposes this is much more representative than the customary average. Statistically both the usual "average" and the median, as well as certain other somewhat similar measures, are all called "averages." To distinguish the particular one commonly used (the sum of the items divided by the number of items) the term "arithmetic average" is used. When the arithmetic average and the median differ this may be a significant fact worth a further look. If in a certain state the arithmetic average high school has 256 pupils, but the median size is 171 pupils, one can with a little reasoning see that half the high schools have less than 171 pupils where there must be a few, perhaps only one or two, large high schools which make the arithmetic average equal to 256.

Galton was a "born statistician." It is due to him more than any other man that attributes of every nature and kind have been reduced to measurement. His influence upon the educational system of the United States is profound. It was his firm belief that until data could be reduced to measurement one could not say that the subject had the dignity of a science. He died at the age of eighty-nine, his keen-penetrating mind remaining active until the last.

Mendel: Peas Make History

Gregor Johann Mendel (1822–1884, Austrian) was born in the same year as Galton but his parents were very poor, whereas Galton's family amassed quite a fortune. Mendel's parents and sisters made many sacrifices to enable him to go to school. He was timid by nature and felt a monastery would be a good place for pursuing an undisturbed life. He received security there and was allowed to have a plot of land on which to make experiments. On a garden strip 120 feet long and about 20 feet wide Mendel grew many and varied pea plants. By a meticulous cross-breeding he arrived at some astounding conclusions. These are oversimplified as follows: Inherited characteristics are carried by genes which appear in pairs.

Inherited characteristics had been studied by others, but Mendel was the first to see that one must not concentrate on the entire organism, but on just one characteristic at a time. By a fortunate coincidence the characteristics he studied were ones suitable for the development of his theory. His experiments led him to two simple but key facts about heredity. First, one trait such as smooth pods can dominate and thus prevent the outward appearance of another trait such as wrinkled pods. The second property is that even though a particular pea may appear to be smooth the factor for wrinkled pods is not destroyed and may reappear in future generations. This holds for other properties as well. Previously it had been thought that mixing would produce a blend as when one mixes two liquids of different colors, but Mendel showed this not to be the case with peas. The following diagram shows the way in which probability enters in:

Distribution of Peas

 Let this symbol represent smooth and yellow, using the characteristics *XXYY*.

Let this symbol represent wrinkled and green, using the characteristics *xxyy*.

No color represents yellow and the shaded area represents green. The capital letters designate the dominant traits. In other words if an *Xx* occurs the characteristic of the *X* would be the one seen.

Suppose the following are the parent peas:

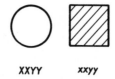

XXYY   xxyy

By the laws of probability and heredity we have $2 \times 2 \times 2 \times 2 = 16$ different combinations as shown:

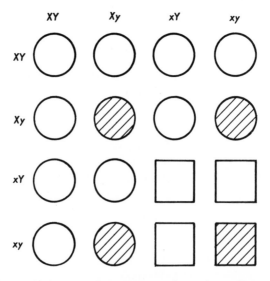

Mendel noted that on the average when the yellow smooth pea was crossed with the green wrinkled pea their offspring appeared in the ratio of (9:3:3:1), that is, by an outward appearance there were nine yellow smooth peas, three green smooth peas, three yellow wrinkled peas and one green wrinkled pea. In the offspring of each of these, however, the recessive traits would reappear, again by the laws of probability and heredity.

There are many characteristics and traits which blend, but in the particular pea experiment described such is not the case.

Mendel gave a presentation of his studies at two meetings of the Natural History Society of Brünn, Austria, but the more he talked about mathematics and formulas the less the attention he was given by his audience. We have here an example of negative or inverse correlation.

Mendel was very disillusioned and the last ten years of his life were embittered by the neglect of a disappointed man. Some say that if Darwin had known of Mendel's discoveries the development of the nineteenth century biological sciences would have been altered. The Mendelian principles have not only played important roles in botany but also in the inherited characteristics of animals as well.

Maxwell: The Greatest Theoretical Physicist of the Nineteenth Century

James Clerk Maxwell (1831–1879, Scotch) in his forty-eight years advanced the field of physics and mathematics in many respects. Maxwell loved to compose verse on scientific matters. As a child he continually wanted to know about everything, and if his elders answered his questions in vague terms, he would pursue his inquiries further until he obtained an answer to his satisfaction.

His health was always delicate, but if he remained at home from school he filled the day by studying on his own. Maxwell worked on the stability of Saturn's rings and became subsequently interested in the kinetic theory of gases. Thus astronomy was indirectly responsible for one of the most extensive scientific applications of probability in the last few centuries. His theory of gases was deduced from the actual velocity of any molecule selected at random. Maxwell showed that the speeds distributed among the molecules were according to the law of errors in a group of observations. The theory is complicated but is a direct application of the theory of probability.

In honor of his work a unit of magnetic flux, the maxwell, is named for him. He also studied color and color blindness, and made wireless telegraphy possible. His title of "Founder of Modern Physics" is justly deserved.

Pearson: Mr. Statistics

Karl Pearson (1857–1936, English) is probably better known than any other individual for his work in the many concepts and methods of statistics. He abandoned the study of law for mathematics and taught for many years. His lectures were very popular, and he illustrated them with a wealth of drawings and diagrams. Among the subjects he taught were the theory of probability and a course in the history of statistics. His intense interest in students was slightly offset by the fact that he became absorbed in the subjects which were interesting to him and practically ignored those in which he had no interest. Other students reported that his methods were secondary only to his personality. He applied statistical methods to problems of a biological nature and termed the resulting science *biometry.*

Pearson did a great deal to extend the study of correlation. He worked in particular with special situations where the usual methods do not apply. The most commonly encountered method of measuring correlation is usually given Pearson's name, although Bravais is entitled to considerable credit for its development. Pearson worked with many other facets in the field of statistics, as for example in the development of tables to facilitate the work and in the mathematical analysis of different types of distributions.

Pearson and his associates vigorously applied statistical methods to evolution, heredity, and related fields, and it was thus by the end of the nineteenth century that the theory of mathematical probability became associated with statistics.

Probability may be applied to everyday events of life. Pearson, in a lecture, described the situation experienced by a friend leaving at a certain time and asked what is the probability that he will find a cab? Is it that he is sure to find one, possible that he will, perhaps, or improbable? In each case there is a rough kind of statistics which is based on the previous experience one had in finding a cab at a certain place at a certain time. It is actually a measure of the confidence we might reasonably expect in the situation.

Weldon: The Dice Tosser

Walter Frank Raphael Weldon (1860–1906, English) was a very good friend of Karl Pearson, and along with Galton and Pearson was co-editor of *Biometrika*. At one time Weldon and Pearson were both teaching at University College and lunched together often. It is said that each lunch table was the scene of many a friendly battle in which pennies were tossed, bread crumbs arranged, and menus or bread used to further arguments. Weldon described deviations from the median as did Galton and calculated the first coefficients of correlation between two characteristics in the same individual.

A classic experiment was made by Weldon in which twelve dice were tossed 4096 times. When the four, five, or six appeared it was considered a success and the numbers were recorded as follows:

No. of Successes	No. of Throws	Expected Frequency or Theoretical No. of Throws
0	0	1
1	7	12
2	60	66
3	198	220
4	430	495
5	731	792
6	948	924
7	847	792
8	536	495
9	257	220
10	71	66
11	11	12
12	0	1
Total	4096	4096

A success, defined as a 4, a 5, or a 6, occurred a total of 25,145 times out of 4096 × 12 throws. The number of successes in all are found by multiplying the number of individual successes by the number of times this occurred. Since 12 dice were thrown 4096 times, this is the same as throwing one die 49,152 times. We now find an experimental probability of 25,145/49,152 = 0.512. On the other hand since the die is assumed to be a true die, the numbers 4, 5, or 6 should come up three times out of 6, so the theoretical probability is 1/2 or 0.500. It is assumed that if the tossing were continued, a person might expect the experimental probability to approach the theoretical value, although as was pointed out, it will not with an increased number of tosses always get closer to the theoretical probability.

Weldon has been described as a brilliant lecturer and was gifted with the power of exciting enthusiasm among his students. His leisure was spent on long bicycle rides around the neighborhood where he studied fauna. He died at the age of forty-six, after a short illness.

Spearman's "G"

Charles Spearman (1863–1945, English) was a psychologist who saw that he needed statistics for his studies and thereby went to work in this field. To Spearman we owe the application of modern statistics to the problem of measuring human faculties. A person's "G" score is usually thought of as his intelligence, but this could also be his concentration, his will power, or even his mental energy.

Pearson's methods for computing the coefficient of correlation are sometimes not applicable when the sample is small or in psychological or educational fields where only the order is known. For example, we might know six different shades of red and could put them in order of their darkness or lightness but could not assign a specific value to them. In these cases we may use methods which were developed by Spearman. The details are available in several books on the subject of educational statistics.

Gosset: The "Student"

William Sealy Gosset (1876–1937, English) is better known under the name of "Student." He was a statistician for a famous Irish brewery which did not then allow publication of research done by its staff, possibly through fear that the stockholders might disapprove of spending money on pure research. The rule was finally relaxed for him but only on the condition that he use a pen name. He chose the name "Student." It is rather paradoxical that today the name of Gosset is scarcely known, though the name "Student" is highly celebrated in the history of statistics.

His original appointment in the brewery was due to the policy of attaching to the staff several university scientists, and it is believed that his interest in statistics was thus aroused. A huge mass of statistical data was at his disposal which had relation to brewing methods and characteristics of the raw material used, together with the quality of the finished product. Gosset was one of the first to realize that this could be applied to the study of the theory of probability. Since the nature of his work called for a short series of experiments, he was led to the study of small samples. One modern form of his work is known as the T-test.

He was a personal friend of Karl Pearson and wrote many papers which were published in *Biometrika,* several of which were edited by Pearson. His writings showed common sense as well as mathematical genius. In much of his theoretical work he resorted to brilliant guesses, where the mathematics barely missed giving a solution. His energy was endless and after returning from a hard day's work he would further pursue his studies.

His collected works contain studies on the testing of varieties of cereals, mathematics, agronomy, and numerous other topics. One experiment was performed on the balanced arrangements of field plots. Field plots refer to small plots of ground used in agricultural experiments such as the study of the effect of different fertilizers. Gosset was the type of man who seemed to profit by his work in industry where he obtained first-hand experience. He toured the fields before harvest and worked with the men themselves to help them improve their barley crop.

Gosset was still in his intellectual prime when he died, and he could have added even more to statistics had he lived but a few more years.

Fisher and the Tea-Tasting Lady

Ronald A. Fisher (1890–   , English) has been called the real giant in the development of the theory of statistics. His work is voluminous and even though there are many workers in the field, he is credited with at least half the esssential and important developments in statistics.

His treatise "Mathematics of a Lady Tasting Tea" deals with the design of experiments or in other words the nature of scientific inquiry itself. This theory is broader than the theory of errors with which Gauss and others worked. Whereas Gauss' theory of errors dealt with limits within which one might expect errors, Fisher's theory takes into account the experiment itself in order to assure that its structure is logical. Former experimenters had to their advantage the fact that their experiments were not as complicated as many have now become. In the above treatise, the tea-tasting lady claims she can tell by tasting a cup of tea made with milk whether the tea or the milk went into the cup first. By using this hypothetical case, Fisher is able to display a series of experiments.

The problem then is to design an experiment with which to test the truth of her claim. The experiment is laid down and its limitations and characteristics discussed. For this particular case he uses eight cups of tea, four mixed in one way and four in another. The subject is aware of this arrangement. The eight cups are then presented to the lady in a random fashion— in other words the order of presentation of the cups is purely a chance order. One question arises: How many different orders of presenting the cups are there? This and similar questions have been discussed previously. If the eight cups were all different we could choose the first cup in eight ways, the second in seven ways, and so on, and there would be $8 \times 7 \times$

$6 \times 5 \times 4 \times 3 \times 2 \times 1$ ways. However, for our purposes we will use four cups alike (milk in the cup first) and four others alike (tea in the cup first). We must divide by the number of ways these cups can be arranged, that is, by $4 \times 3 \times 2 \times 1$ and again by $4 \times 3 \times 2 \times 1$. There are then seventy different arrangements for the eight cups.

A person having no facility for distinguishing the order in which the milk was placed in the cup would on the average be expected to get the correct order $1/70$ of the time. As the number of cups increases, the less would be the probability of obtaining the correct order by pure chance. No matter how carefully the experiment is designed, and no matter how many cups are used, there is always the possibility that the correct order might be obtained by pure chance, whether or not there is any real ability to distinguish any difference. The experimenter must then decide what allowance shall be made for pure chance. If the experiment is so designed that there is less than one chance in 100 that a correct result would be obtained by the operation of chance alone, the results may be said to be significant at the 1 per cent level. The experiment could be designed so that the eight cups are used, but the trial is repeated more than once; or there may be more than eight cups used. Then it is necessary to decide how many correct responses must be obtained before one concludes that the lady can truly make the distinction, rather than making correct responses by pure chance. It must be remembered that it is never possible to have identical conditions. Such things as slight temperature changes as a function of the time the tea was poured or almost imperceptible differences in thickness or smoothness of the cup, and so forth, must be taken into consideration.

We have now brought the discussion of probability and statistics up to the present time. In the next chapter we shall review and expand the overall applications which may occur from these subjects.

13

Applying Probability

Unfortunately many people hold the mistaken concept that the only applications of probability are in the field of gambling. As has been shown, nothing could be farther from the truth. It is the purpose of this chapter to show additional places where probability furnishes some very useful and important results.

Chapter 5 dealt briefly with the use of probability in the fields of life insurance and life annuities. There are many kinds of insurance, all of which depend basically upon the concepts of probability. The first type of insurance to be developed was marine insurance, which involved sharing the risk of the loss of a ship and its cargo in a disaster at sea. Fundamentally, such insurance consisted of a group of individuals joining together to share a small loss, rather than run the risk of individually suffering a large loss.

Probability enters when by study of statistics about losses at sea there is a determination of the statistical or empirical probability that a ship of a certain type will be lost. The same principle holds with other types of insurance. If, for example, it is known that in a certain city an average of 110 automobiles out of 16,000 registered are stolen each year, then the probability that Mr. Roe, a resident of that city, will have his car stolen next year is 0.006875. If he wishes to insure his car against theft for the sum of $3000 it would be reasonable to charge a premium of $20.63 plus whatever sum is needed to cover office expenses and profit for the insurance company.

If data show that one house out of 800 of a certain type is destroyed each year by fire, and a man desires to carry $7200 of insurance on such a house for one year, the "net" premium would be $9.00. The term "net" premium is used to designate that portion required by applying the laws of empirical probability, exclusive of any amounts added for expenses, commission to agents, or profits. Groups planning important outdoor events often take out insurance against the necessity of canceling the event because of rain. The cost of such insurance is based on empirical probability; the probability of rain is based on records of the weather bureau for past years at the spot in question. If in a certain city records show that over the past fifteen years appreciable amounts of rain have fallen on two days out of the first sixteen of July, the empirical probability of rain on July Fourth is determined to be 2/16 or 1/8. If the County Fair Association wishes rain insurance of $8000 to cover their Fourth of July program, the "net" premium would be $1000. The amount may seem high, but actually it means they exchange a certain expenditure of $1000 for a possible complete loss of $8000 in business.

Some individuals carry insurance against accidental death, either in the form of added insurance in connection with a regular insurance policy, or a special accident insurance policy. Many persons purchase accident insurance when taking a trip by airplane. The cost seems quite small for a very appreciable amount of coverage, but it must be remembered that the period of coverage is usually a single trip which amounts to a fraction of a day. If one considers the large number of trips which are made safely, it is evident that the probability of the death of a passenger is quite small. The insurance company has made a careful study of probability before establishing the cost of insurance.

If there has been observation of a coin tossing game, and the coin has landed "heads" four times in a row, many people will rush to bet that the next time it will be "tails." They overlook the fact that a coin has no memory and keeps no records. If the coin is true and the tossing has been honest, the probability of "heads" on the fifth toss is exactly the same as on the first toss, that is, 1/2. To the person who believes otherwise, one might direct the question: How can you ever determine the probability for a single toss, since you do not know the result of the previous tosses for this coin whenever they may have occurred. One must note that this question is entirely different than asking the probability of five successive heads before a single toss has been made. Here the probability is $(1/2)^5$ or $1/32$. A related question, involving somewhat more careful analysis arises when one asks for the probability that the fifth child, about to arrive in a family, will be a girl, it being known that the preceding four children were girls. Careless drawing of a parallel with the coin tossing would yield the answer one-half. However the probability of a female birth is not one-half, but slightly less than one-half. Again it is possible that the previous four births, all girls, might be slight justification for the determination of an empirical probability that this particular family has a greater tendency toward female births. In other words, the successive births may not be independent events.

Manufacturers are often very anxious that their product be as nearly perfect as possible. Elaborate inspection procedures are often established. Many manufacturers will at first state that they will accept nothing less than 100 percent inspection, that is, they will demand inspection of every item. But even with expert workers and careful inspection a defective item may occasionally slip through. The problem becomes much more complicated when inspection requires destruction of the product.

Consider the manufacturer who is making household electric fuses to carry fifteen amperes. An effective way of testing such fuses would be to place each fuse in a circuit and make sure it would carry fifteen amperes of current without blowing. Then, to be sure it is an effective safety device, the current should be increased to some amount in excess of fifteen amperes. If the fuse is properly made it will blow. Even if we overlook the cost of testing every fuse among thousands made, the test has destroyed the fuse and the manufacturer has nothing left to sell. The same reasoning would hold for the manufacturer of artillery shells.

It seems obvious that in some way a method must be developed which will permit testing a relatively small number of items, yet allow conclusions to be drawn about the items not

tested. If the manufacturer of fuses tests one fuse out of every
500 manufactured and finds less than 2 percent defective
is he justified in assuming that less than 2 percent of the
entire lot is defective? This involves several questions. First,
is the sample a random one; has very fuse an equal chance of
being selected? Secondly, what is the probability that if the
sample shows 2 percent defective, the lot will not exceed
3 percent defective, or will not exceed 5 percent, or will
not be less than 1 percent? Questions such as this are
considered in the commercial use of probability in a sampling
situation. A somewhat related question is: How large a sample
must be taken in order to have less than one chance in one
hundred that the value obtained from the sample does not
differ by more than a given amount from that of the group
from which the sample is taken. A comparatively recent development is the concept of sequential sampling.

In a somewhat simplified illustration, assume a manufacturer is willing to accept a shipment of articles provided there
are not more than 3 percent of the items defective. He
selects a relatively small number of items and examines them.
If the number of defective items exceeds 5 percent, the
entire shipment is rejected; if the number defective is less than
1 percent, the entire shipment is accepted. For a value
between these limits, the sampling process is continued, obtaining a larger number of items to be inspected. If the total
number of items sampled shows more than 4 percent, the entire
shipment is rejected, and if less than 2 percent the shipment is
accepted. The process may be continued, or at some stage
acceptance or rejection may be set at the 3 percent line.

It is, of course, true that the process of sampling may cause
a shipment to be accepted when actually the percent of defective items is more than the figure set in the contract between buyer and seller. This is known as a "buyer's risk."
Again the sampling process might cause rejection of a shipment which actually was within the specifications. This is
known as "seller's risk." Concepts of probability are used in
an attempt to be as fair as possible to everyone concerned.

The determination of the percent of defective items which

will be specified in the contract sometimes involves the use of probability to find the cost of replacement. A defective small cogwheel used in the interior assembly of a delicate instrument may be much more serious than a defective screw used in installing the instrument on a control panel. The cogwheel may require a complete reassembly of the instrument at considerable expense; the defective screw can be replaced at relatively little cost. The probability of certain expenditures, depending upon the particular defective item may require considerable study.

For another illustration of a problem involving probability let us consider the problem faced by the purchasing agent of a large company. He wishes to purchase a large quantity of light bulbs, and has reached a place where a decision must be made between the products of two companies, each a reputable concern. Prices being equal he decides to base his decision upon the average length of life of the two makes of bulbs. He obtains a random sample of 200 bulbs from each company and puts them in use under conditions such as exist in his firm. A record is kept of the number of hours each bulb lasts, either the time until the bulb burns out or the time it takes for the light emitted from the bulb to decrease to 75 percent or less of that light given by a new bulb. This will be considered a worn-out bulb from the efficiency point of view. Supposing the average length of life for bulbs made by company A is 1240 hours, while for company B the average length of life is 1300 hours. Does this imply that bulbs made by company B have a longer average length of life? If the experiment were repeated, could he be sure the difference would again be in favor of company B? Or is it possible that this time bulbs from company A would have a longer average length of life? It may be stated that it is impossible ever to be absolutely certain. It is conceivable that even if bulbs from company B are definitely of longer life there might be one chance in a thousand that the sampling process produced a very unusual sample in which bulbs from company A seem superior. However, again the theory of probability enters the picture. It seems reasonable to adopt a rule in common use: If there are less than five chances in one hundred that the actual situation differs from that shown in the sample, it is not unreasonable to think that the results obtained from the sample are acceptable and could be used as a basis of decision. Technically we speak of the difference as being "significant at the 5 percent level."

Even though we may have a situation where there is only one chance in one hundred that the situation, as shown from the sample, differs from that which would exist if all items could have been studied, it follows that there will be one chance in one hundred in which the sample gives an erroneous picture. It sometimes happens that the erroneous picture occurs in situations very embarrassing to the statistician.

This concept of sampling and the accompanying application of the laws of probability find extensive use in polls; public opinion polls; polls to determine what radio or television program is being watched or listened to; polls to determine housewives' reactions to a new product; political polls, and the like. In most cases the sampling is carefully planned and often a margin of error is stated. Polls cannot, however, altogether eliminate the fact that certain people dislike being questioned and may deliberately conceal or give false information. In spite of this and other objections, the method of sampling often makes results available in situations where the cost of a complete enumeration would be prohibitive both from the standpoint of time and of money.

Thus we can see that probability and statistics are used in insurance, physics, genetics, biology, business, as well as in games of chance; and we are inclined to agree with P. S. Laplace who said: "We see . . . that the theory of probabilities is at bottom only common sense reduced to calculation; it makes us appreciate with exactitude what reasonable minds feel by a sort of instinct, often without being able to account for it . . . . It is remarkable that [this] science, which originated in the consideration of games of chance, should have become the most important object of human knowledge."

Bibliography

General History:

Ball, W. W. Rouse, *A Short Account of the History of Mathematics*. New York: Dover Publications, Inc., 1960, 522 pp.
A very good standard reference is found in this book.

Bell, E. T., *The Development of Mathematics*. New York: McGraw-Hill Book Company, Inc., 1940, 583 pp.
The historical approach is broken down into the different fields, enabling one to more quickly find information on a certain concept.

Bell, E. T., *Men of Mathematics*. New York: Simon and Schuster, 1937, 590 pp.
This book is a classic and one of the best to be found in describing the several mathematicians who are discussed. A sense of humor combined with many enlightening facts makes a work which can be highly recommended.

Cajori, Florian, *A History of Mathematics*. New York: The Macmillan Company, 1924, 516 pp.
If one desires facts which are sometimes hard to find, this would be a good place to look. It is so factual, however, that at times it is a little monotonous.

Dunnington, G. Waldo, *Carl Friedrich Gauss: Titan of Science*. New York: Exposition Press, 1955, 479 pp.
An interesting biography of Gauss is to be found here.

Clarke, Frances Marguerite, *Thomas Simpson and His Times*. New York: Waverly Press, Inc., 1929, 215 pp.
An interesting story of Thomas Simpson, this book shows what the times were during his life. Some of the examples are long and involved.

Newman, James R., *The World of Mathematics*, Vols. 1, 2, 3, 4. New York: Simon and Schuster, 1956, 2535 pp.
One will find here an excellent reference as well as ample interesting reading in the field of mathematics. Inasmuch as Mr. Newman admits his partiality to the theory of probability and statistics, these books are especially recommended.

Ore, Oystein, *Cardano*. Princeton: Princeton University Press,
1953, 249 pp.
Mr. Ore presents a wealth of entertainment and knowledge
in this book which gives an insight into Cardano's life.

Rukeyser, Muriel, *Willard Gibbs*. Garden City: Doubleday,
Doran & Company, Inc., 1942, 465 pp.
This book is recommended for one wishing any further
knowledge about the life of Gibbs.

Scott, J. F., *A History of Mathematics*. London: Taylor &
Francis, Ltd., 1958, 266 pp.
This is another good history of mathematics.

Scott, J. F., *The Mathematical Work of John Wallis*. London:
Taylor and Francis, Ltd., 1938, 240 pp.
Insight is given here into the life and work of John Wallis.
Some of the information, however, would be considered above
the secondary level.

Smith, David Eugene, *History of Mathematics*, Vols. 1 and 2.
New York: Dover Publications, Inc., 1958, Vol. 1, 596 pp.,
Vol. 2, 725 pp.
These books comprise some of the very best that have been
written in the general history of mathematics. They are very
complete and interesting and are old stand-bys in the field.

Todhunter, I., *A History of the Mathematical Theory of
Probability*. New York: G. E. Stechert & Co., 1931, 624 pp.
This is recommended as a general outline of probability.

Walker, Helen M., *Studies in the History of Statistical Method*.
Baltimore: The Williams & Wilkins Company, 1931, 229 pp.
Many little-known anecdotes are found in this work, plus an
interesting account of the history of probability and the way
it led into statistics.

Wiener, Norbert, *Ex-Prodigy*. New York: Simon and Schuster,
1953, 309 pp.

Wiener, Norbert, *I Am a Mathematician*. Garden City: Doubleday & Company, Inc., 1956, 380 pp.
Both of the books by Dr. Wiener are highly recommended for
a student wishing to learn and relive adventures of childhood
or trials of a learned mathematician. They are both inspiring,
interesting, and informative.

Concepts of Probability:

Feller, William, *An Introduction to Probability Theory* and Its
Applications. New York: John Wiley & Sons, Inc., 1950,
461 pp.
Probability can become very complicated very quickly, but
there are many parts of this book which would be elucidating.

Fry, Thornton C., *Probability and Its Engineering Uses*. New York: D. Van Nostrand Company, Inc., 1928, 470 pp.

The same comment applies here as to the previous reference.

Goldberg, Samuel, *Probability*. Englewood Cliffs, N.J.: Prentice-Hall, Inc., 1960, 322 pp.

This book presents a more elementary treatment than many of its kind.

Jeffreys, Harold, *Theory of Probability*. Oxford: The Clarendon Press, 1948, 411 pp.

This is another good standard reference on the theory of probability.

Levinson, Horace C. *The Science of Chance*. New York: Holt, Rinehart and Winston, Inc., 1950, 348 pp.

This book may be read almost like a novel, and is a most interesting presentation of the subject of probability. It is highly recommended to the reader desiring further knowledge on the subject.

Mosteller, Frederick, Robert E. K. Rourke, and George B. Thomas, Jr., *Probability and Statistics*. Reading, Mass.: Addison-Wesley Publishing Company, Inc., 1961, 395 pp.

This was the official textbook for Continental Classroom, a recent course on television. It is a good general treatise.

"Student's" Collected Papers, (Edited by E. S. Pearson and John Wishart.) London: University Press, 1947, 224 pp.

Although much of the information here presented is somewhat advanced, other parts are quite readable and would perhaps be of interest to the student wishing to read for himself the actual material written by a worker in the field of probability.

Glossary

Asymptote. A line which limits a branch of a curve in one direction. In a hyperbola, for example, the axes of the graph are the asymptotes of the curve, limiting it in both directions.

Combinations. The total number of different groups that can be formed from a given number of items, order within each group being immaterial.

Conic sections. Plane curves obtained by cutting a circular cone by a plane, at various angles.

Cycloid. A curve represented by the path of a point on the rim of a rolling wheel.

Dependent event. An event is dependent if its occurrence is affected by some other event. If a card it taken from a deck and is not replaced, the probability of a second card being red or black is dependent on the color of the first card.

Independent event. An event is said to be independent if its occurrence is not affected by the occurrence of some other event. If a card is taken from a deck and then replaced in the deck, the probability of a second card being red or black is independent of the color of the first card.

Inverse probability. The concept which relates to the probability of unknown causes which are deduced from observed events.

Mathematical expectation. The product of the probability that an event will happen multiplied by the value of the event.

Mutually exclusive event. Two or more events are mutually exclusive if the occurrence of one event eliminates the possible occurrence of another event. For example, if a coin is tossed and lands "heads," this event excludes the possibility of "tails," since only one of the two possibilities can occur in a single toss.

Odds. The ratio of the number of possible successful events to the number of possible unsuccessful events. Odds should not be confused with probability—the odds of getting a "head" in one toss of a coin are 1:1, the probability of a "head" is 1:2.

Permutations. The total number of different arrangements that can be made of a given number of items.

Statistics. The science of collecting and classifying facts on a basis of relative numbers, as a foundation for induction of general truths.

Index